# Enabling Accessibility Through Kiosk Design

Enabling Accessibility Through Kiosk Design

발  행 | 2023년 11월 29일
저  자 | 배예나
펴낸이 | 한건희
펴낸곳 | 주식회사 부크크
출판사등록 | 2014.07.15.(제2014-16호)
주  소 | 서울특별시 금천구 가산디지털1로 119 SK트윈타워 A동 305호
전  화 | 1670-8316
이메일 | info@bookk.co.kr

ISBN | 979-11-410-5589-9

www.bookk.co.kr

# Enabling Accessibility Through Kiosk Design

배예나 지음

# CONTENT

About the author

1. Introduction to Kiosks and Accessibility

2. How to Make Kiosks Accessible

3. Assistive Technology and Accessibility

4. Universal Design Principles

5. Creating User-Friendly Interfaces

6. Understanding the Accessibility Impact of Your Design

7. Finding a Balance Between Comfort and Convenience

8. How to Test Kiosks for Accessibility

9. The Challenges of Alternative Inputs

10. Designing for Ease of Use

11. Creating an Accessible Keyboard Layout

12. Designing Accessible Non-Text Messages

13. Designing for Visually Impaired People

14. Making Your Kiosks Accessible to Hearing Loss

15. Designing for Dexterity Challenges

16. Designing for Cognitive Disabilities

17. Designing for Multiple Languages

18. Adaption of Kiosks for Different Cultures

19. Ensuring Compliance with Disability Laws

20. Conclusion: Making the Future Accessible for Everyone

배예나 교수는 교육/디자인/공학 전문가로서 다양한 역량과 성과물을 창조해내는 폴리매스이다. 낮에는 대학에서 학생들을 지도하고, 밤에는 새로운 도전과 덕업일치 실현을 위해 프로샐러던트의 삶을 살고 있다. 현재 인제대학교 컴퓨터디자인과 교수로 재직 중이며 베스트셀러 저서로 『메타버스에서 디자이너로 성공하기』와 『게임 디자인 마스터하기』가 있다.

Do you want to learn more about designing kiosks that make life easier for people with disabilities? This book is the perfect guide! It's packed with information about the principles of universal design, creating user-friendly interfaces and understanding the intersection of technology and disability. You'll benefit from expert advice, making it easy to design kiosks that can empower people with disabilities. Read this book, and you'll be on your way to becoming an expert at designing accessible kiosks.

# 1. Introduction to Kiosks and Accessibility

Kiosks are becoming an increasingly common way to access services in today's digital world. This chapter will provide an introduction to kiosks and how they can be used to increase accessibility for all users. We will discuss the different types of assistive technology available for kiosks, potential barriers that may exist, and how to ensure compliance with existing laws and regulations. Through exploring these topics we will learn the important role kiosks can play in making services more accessible and user-friendly. This chapter will provide valuable insights into the challenges and solutions surrounding kiosks, so that all users can benefit from their use.

# ◢ Unlock Accessibility with Kiosks: Why Everyone Should Benefit from Their Use

It was a sunny Saturday morning in the city.  All around people were running errands, chatting with friends and family, and enjoying the day. But for one special person, this day was especially important.

Charlie had been dreaming of this day for months–they finally had an appointment at the local city hall. Unfortunately, the city hall wasn't set up to help people with disabilities like Charlie, and they needed to use the kiosk to complete their paperwork.

The kiosk was frustratingly difficult to use. Charlie had to rely on a friend to help them figure out how to use the buttons and fill out their forms. It felt like a never–ending struggle to get their paperwork complete.

But, despite the difficulties, Charlie persisted–and eventually filled out all the paperwork. By the time they were finished the sun had long since set, and Charlie was exhausted.

But Charlie had done it! They felt such a sense of accomplishment and relief that their dream had finally come true. This experience made Charlie realize the importance of kiosks with accessibility features, so that people with disabilities can benefit equally from services like the one they had just accessed.

## ❑ Introduction to Kiosks and Accessibility

A kiosk is a type of freestanding computer that is designed for public use. It is typically used to provide information or services to customers, such as ticketing, check–in, and payment. Kiosks are versatile and can be used in almost any setting, from airports to malls to stadiums.

When it comes to defining a kiosk, there is no single answer. The design, purpose and features of kiosks can vary immensely. Generally, they are computers with a touchscreen monitor and a specialized user interface. They can include additional features such as a printer, card reader, camera, speakers, and noise cancellation components.

Kiosks can be used for a variety of tasks depending on their purpose. At airports, for example, they are commonly used for ticket purchase, flight check-in and baggage retrieval. Ticketing kiosks are also used in movie theaters, stadiums, and other places of entertainment. Retail kiosks can be used for payment processing and product ordering. Information kiosks are used to provide information to customers, including maps, menus, tourist information and more.

Kiosks can be extremely beneficial to people of all abilities. Their user-friendly interfaces and accessibility features make them perfect for people with disabilities who may have difficulty using more conventional computers. For this reason, it is important to understand the principles of universal design and user-friendly interfaces when designing a kiosk. That way, you can ensure that your kiosks are accessible to everyone.

## ❏ Introduction to Increasing Accessibility Through Kiosks

Using kiosks to increase accessibility is a great way to make sure everyone can enjoy the same user experience. It can also be beneficial to businesses, as having easier access to services and products can create a better customer experience and improved convenience. It's important to understand the benefits of using kiosks for accessibility, as well as some of the common issues that may arise.

## ❏ Benefits of Using Kiosks for Accessibility
When thinking about kiosk design for accessibility, it is important to consider the benefits. Kiosks can provide an improved customer experience, as they can allow customers to access products and services more quickly and easily without having to wait in line. They can also provide greater convenience, as they allow customers to complete tasks on their own without needing assistance. Kiosks can also help create a more inclusive environment, as they can offer access to products and services to those with disabilities.

## ❏ Examples of How Kiosks Improve Accessibility
Kiosks can offer several examples of how to improve accessibility. For example, they can reduce wait times, as customers can complete tasks on their own without assistance or waiting in line. They can also provide easier access to information, as information can be presented in a variety of formats and can be easily accessed through the kiosk. In addition, kiosks can provide improved

8

access to services, as customers with disabilities can use them to access products or services that are normally difficult for them to access.

❏ Common Accessibility Issues
When designing kiosks for accessibility, it is important to note that there are some common issues that may arise. One of the most common issues is a poor user experience, as kiosks may not always be user-friendly and may present challenges for users with disabilities. Additionally, kiosks may present difficulties for users with reading difficulties, as the text may be too complex or too small for them to read. Finally, kiosks may also have complex user interfaces, as they may be difficult to use and may require a certain level of technical knowledge.

❏ Conclusion
When designing kiosks for accessibility, it is important to consider the benefits as well as potential issues. Kiosks can provide an improved customer experience, greater convenience, and easier access to products and services. However, they can present challenges in terms of user experience, reading difficulties, and complexity of user interface. It is therefore important to be aware of these issues when designing kiosks for accessibility.

# Accessibility Considerations in Kiosk Design

When designing a kiosk, accessibility considerations are essential. By taking into account the needs of people with disabilities, you can create a kiosk that is truly accessible and usable for everyone. In this chapter, we will discuss the importance of accessibility considerations in kiosk design, how to design a kiosk to meet accessibility requirements, and the accessibility features to consider.

The importance of accessibility considerations in kiosk design cannot be overstated. By making sure that the kiosk meets the requirements of people with disabilities, you will be able to increase its usability and create a better customer experience for all users. Moreover, compliance with regulations and standards is a must in order to ensure that your kiosk does not face legal action.

In order to design a kiosk that meets accessibility requirements, it is important to set up a user testing process. By testing the accessibility of the kiosk, you will be able to uncover any potential problems or issues that need to be addressed. Additionally, it is important to ensure that the user interface is designed in a way that is easy for users to understand. This may include simplifying menus and instructions, increasing colour contrast, and providing large, clear buttons.

When designing a kiosk, there are a number of accessibility features to consider. These features can include speech recognition, colour contrast, keyboard navigation, and tactile keyboards. Speech recognition allows the kiosk to understand user commands, while colour contrast ensures that people with colour blindness can easily read the text on the screen. Keyboard navigation makes it easier for users to navigate the menus, while tactile keyboards make it easier for users with dexterity challenges to type.

By taking into consideration the needs of people with disabilities, it is possible to create a truly accessible and usable kiosk. By setting up a user testing process, designing user interfaces that are easy to understand, and considering a range of accessibility features, you can ensure that your kiosk meets the requirements of all users. With the right design, you can create an accessible and usable kiosk that offers a better customer experience for everyone.

❑ Introduction to Assistive Technology

When it comes to making kiosks accessible to people with disabilities, assistive technology plays a key role. Assistive technology is any device, piece of software, or system that helps a person with a disability complete daily tasks. It includes a wide range of devices and programs, such as voice recognition, text-to-speech, and screen readers.

❏ Voice Recognition

Voice recognition is a type of technology that helps people with disabilities interact with a kiosk. It is a type of speech recognition software that can interpret what the user is saying and make decisions for them. This technology is especially useful for people who are unable to use a keyboard or mouse.

❏ Text-to-Speech

Text-to-speech is a type of assistive technology that helps people with disabilities interact with a kiosk. Text-to-speech technology can read out loud text that appears on the screen. This is especially useful for people with low vision, as it makes it easier to interact with the kiosk.

❏ Screen Readers

Screen readers are a type of assistive technology that help people with disabilities interact with a kiosk. A screen reader is a type of software that reads out loud the text that appears on the screen. This is especially useful for people with low vision, as it makes it easier to interact with the kiosk.

❏ Choosing the Right Assistive Technology

When it comes to selecting the right assistive technology for a kiosk, it is important to consider the user's needs and the kiosk's customer profile. For example, if the customers are mostly seniors, it would be beneficial to install an adjustable counter and provide a variety of input methods, such as a number keypad. On the other hand, if the customer profile is primarily children, it would be beneficial to install a touchscreen device, or a large and intuitive keyboard.

❏ Benefits of Assistive Technology

The use of assistive technology for kiosks can have many benefits, such as improved accessibility, customer experience, and ease of use. In addition, when designed properly, it can help ensure that the kiosk meets legal requirements, such as the Americans with Disabilities Act (ADA).

❑ Conclusion

In conclusion, the use of assistive technology is an important part of making kiosks accessible to people with disabilities. It can help ensure that customers can use the kiosk in a safe and convenient manner. When selecting the right assistive technology, it is important to consider the user's needs and the kiosk's customer profile, as well as the legal requirements. By doing so, we can make sure that everyone has the same opportunity to access the kiosk.

❑ Potential Barriers

When considering how to design a kiosk that is accessible to everyone, it is important to consider potential barriers that someone with a disability may face. These barriers can be physical, communication, or cognitive.

❑ Physical Barriers

Physical barriers can include anything that makes it difficult for someone with a disability to access or operate the kiosk. This may include the size and location of the kiosk, the height of the counter or display, and the type of input device. To address physical barriers, it is important to make sure the kiosk can be adjusted to fit the person correctly. This includes adjustable counters, and adjustable keyboards or number pads.

❑ Communication Barriers

Communication barriers can include difficulty reading or understanding the text and graphics displayed on the kiosk. To address this, it is important to ensure that the text and graphics are designed to be easy to understand, and to include a variety of linguistic options, such as voice and text commands.

❑ Cognitive Barriers

Cognitive barriers can include difficulty understanding how to use the kiosk. To address this, it is important to keep the user interface simple and easy to understand, and to provide clear, step-by-step instructions. Additionally, it is important to consider assistive technologies such as text-to-speech, touchscreens, speech recognition, tactile keyboards, and voice recognition.

❑ Examples of Accessibility Solutions

There are a variety of accessibility solutions that can be incorporated into kiosk design. Adjustable counters can be set up to accommodate different heights and wheelchairs. Number keypads can be used to make it easier for those with cognitive or dexterity issues to enter information. Text-to-speech systems can help to make the kiosk more accessible to those with reading difficulties or visual impairments. Touchscreens can make it easier for those with dexterity issues to access information. Speech recognition systems can also help to make the kiosk easier to use, by allowing the user to speak their commands instead of typing them. Additionally, adjustable keyboards can be used to make typing easier for those with dexterity issues. Finally, linguistic options can be used to make the kiosk more accessible to those with different language backgrounds.

In conclusion, it is important to take into account potential barriers when designing a kiosk. This includes physical, communication, and cognitive barriers. Additionally, it is important to consider various accessibility solutions, such as adjustable counters, number keypads, text-to-speech, touchscreens, speech recognition, tactile keyboards, adjustable keyboards, and linguistic options. By taking these issues into account, you can ensure that your kiosk is accessible to everyone.

❑ Legal Requirements for Kiosk Accessibility

Whenever designing a kiosk, it is important to have a good understanding of the legal requirements and standards for making the kiosk accessible. In the United States, the Americans with Disabilities Act (ADA) sets out the standards for providing access to public facilities and services. The ADA Accessibility Guidelines (ADAAG) apply to any part of a building that the public uses, including kiosks. These guidelines are designed to ensure that people with disabilities can access and use the same services as everyone else.

When designing a kiosk, there are various legal requirements that must be met. These requirements cover everything from a kiosk's physical design, to the way it is used, to the accessibility features it provides. Knowledge of the legal requirements will help ensure that the kiosk is designed with the needs of disabled people in mind.

When designing a kiosk, it is important to ensure that the kiosk meets all of the accessibility standards set out in the ADAAG. This includes using the right size and height of the kiosk, making sure it is easy to reach, and providing an interface that can be used easily by people with disabilities. It is also important to consider the impact of the kiosk on the surrounding environment, to make sure it is not creating any unnecessary barriers to accessibility.

Once the kiosk has been designed, it is important to test it to ensure that it meets the legal requirements. This testing process should include having test users with disabilities use the kiosk, and collecting feedback from them. This is the best way to make sure that the kiosk meets all the legal requirements for accessibility.

Failure to comply with the legal requirements for kiosk accessibility can lead to serious repercussions, including fines, legal proceedings, or other disciplinary action. It is important, therefore, to ensure that the kiosk is designed and tested to meet all applicable legal requirements.

By understanding the legal requirements and taking the necessary steps to ensure that the kiosk meets those requirements, businesses and organizations can ensure that their kiosks are accessible to everyone. This will improve the customer experience and make sure that disabled people can access the same services as everyone else. Ensuring that kiosks are accessible not only meets the legal requirements, but it is also the right thing to do.

❑ Conclusion

This chapter provided an introduction to the concept of kiosks and accessibility. It discussed the importance of considering accessibility when designing a kiosk, especially the use of assistive technology to ensure that individuals with disabilities can interact with the kiosk. It also discussed potential barriers that need to be taken into consideration such as the physical size of the kiosk, visual design, and the legal requirements for making kiosks accessible. Ultimately, a well-designed kiosk should be accessible to everyone, regardless of their abilities.

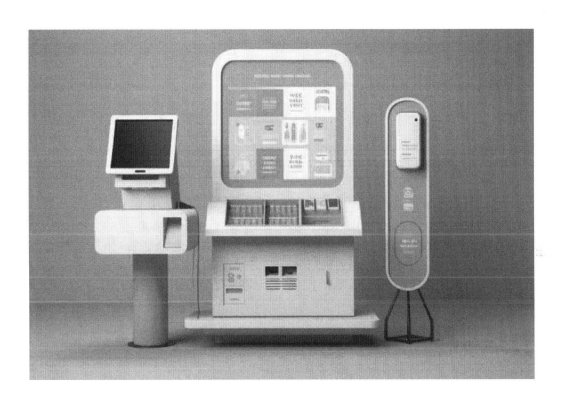

# ◥ Examples of Kiosks That Can Enhance Accessibility For You

Person One: Mark had a disability that made it difficult for him to go out in public. He owned a small LEGO store and wanted to make it more accessible for his customers. To do this, he installed a kiosk with an accessible button layout, voice activation, and a large monitor. This allowed customers with disabilities to easily shop in his store.

Person Two: Jane runs a retail clothing shop. She wanted to make sure that her customer base was as large as possible, including people with disabilities. To do this, she installed a kiosk with a voice-controlled navigation system, Braille printouts, and a headset with a microphone. This allowed customers with disabilities to easily purchase items from her shop.

Person Three: Joe wanted to make sure his restaurant was accessible to everyone. He installed a kiosk with adjustable screen height, tactile buttons and large print menus. People with disabilities could now easily order food from the restaurant. Joe also added a large-print receipt printer, so that customers with low vision could read their bill.

# ◥ Step-by-Step List: Examples of Kiosks That Can Enhance Accessibility For You

1. What a kiosk is:
- Research the history of kiosk design
- Identify the purpose of kiosks in the present day

2. The role of kiosks in increasing accessibility:
- Learn the different ways that kiosks can be used to improve accessability
- Analyze the various benefits of using kiosks to increase accessibility

3. The importance of accessibility considerations when designing a kiosk:
- Examine how to design a kiosk interface that can be used by all people, regardless of ability
- Explore how to make the kiosk intuitive and user friendly
- Understand the importance of making content accessible

4. The different types of assistive technology used with kiosks:

- Identify the different kinds of assistive technology available for use with kiosks

- Consider different ways that these technologies can be used to enhance kiosk use for those with disabilities

5. Potential barriers that need to be considered when designing a kiosk:

- Understand how common barriers such as lighting and sound can affect kiosk use

- Learn how to design a kiosk that is free of accessibility barriers

6. The legal requirements for making kiosks accessible:

- Research the applicable accessibility laws

- Develop a plan to ensure that the kiosk design meets the legal requirements

## ◼ Learning the Framework of Kiosks to Enhance Your Accessibility

The 5D Framework for Accessible Kiosk Design:

1. Discover: Gather data and understand the customer needs and the legal requirements for kiosks.

2. Design: Come up with a design that makes the kiosk as accessible as possible.

3. Develop: Create the kiosk with the accessible design in mind.

4. Deploy: Test the kiosk in a variety of situations to ensure it works effectively.

5. Dedicate: Regularly monitor and maintain the kiosk to ensure it remains accessible.

## ◼ Common Mistakes in Designing Accessible Kiosks: What to Avoid

One of the biggest mistakes people make when designing kiosks for people with disabilities is overlooking how the kiosk will be used. People often think that simply making the kiosk accessible is enough, but this is not the case. Accessibility is about more than just the physical design - it's about creating a user experience that enables people with disabilities to successfully use the kiosk. This means understanding how the kiosk will be used, considering the needs of the user and incorporating assistive technology where needed.

Another mistake people make is failing to consider the environment in which the kiosk is situated. The physical environment can have a big impact on the usability of the kiosk - for example, if the kiosk is situated in a busy or crowded area it should be placed in a way that allows enough space for people to use it without obstruction. This could be achieved by using non-obstructive barriers or carefully placed signage. It's also important to consider the light and sound levels in the vicinity of the kiosk - ensuring that the environment is not too noisy or too dark for people to effectively use the kiosk.

The accessibility of the kiosk should also extend beyond the physical design. It's important to consider the language, tone and style of the kiosk interface, as these can all impact how effective the kiosk is for users. It's also important to consider the needs of users with different levels of assistive technology - for example, people who are vision impaired may need text to speech enabled and those with hearing impairments may need captions.

Finally, people often overlook the legal requirements for making kiosks accessible. Depending on the environment in which a kiosk is placed, certain legal requirements may need to be met. This could be anything from complying with the Americans with Disabilities Act (ADA) to local regulations. It's important to make sure you understand the applicable legal requirements and that the kiosk meets these before it is deployed.

In conclusion, there are a number of non-obvious mistakes people make when designing kiosks for people with disabilities. Overlooking user needs, failing to consider the environment, not accounting for different levels of assistive technology, and not understanding the applicable legal requirements are some of the biggest mistakes. Understanding these mistakes can help people design more effective and usable kiosks that enable people with disabilities to use them successfully.

# 2. How to Make Kiosks Accessible

This chapter will provide an in-depth look at the ways in which kiosks can be designed to be as accessible as possible. We will explore the needs and requirements of people with disabilities, the regulations and guidelines related to accessibility, and the methods for evaluating and designing a kiosk for the best possible user experience. You will acquire the knowledge you need to select the appropriate hardware, software, and peripherals for the kiosk, as well as analyze ways to make kiosks easier for people with disabilities to use. This chapter is designed to give you the insight needed to make your kiosks more accessible for everyone and create a better user experience.

# Why Kiosk Accessibility is Important for Everyone

❑ The setting is a busy train station, near the ticket kiosks.

The character is a young man in a wheelchair named Alex. He is on his way to a job interview, and he's late due in part to the extra time it took him to find a station with a wheelchair accessible kiosk. He sees the kiosks, but the ones he needs are all out of his reach.

Alex is desperate, as he realizes he may miss his chance at the job if he doesn't get his ticket soon. He looks around helplessly and notices an older gentleman who notices his struggles. The gentleman immediately comes to his rescue, and helps Alex buy his ticket from a kiosk that was designed to be accessible to those with disabilities.

With the help of the kind stranger, Alex makes it to his job interview, which ends up being a success, leading to a new career path. The experience gives Alex a newfound appreciation for the importance of accessible kiosks, making his dream of becoming independent a reality.

❑ Understanding the Needs and Requirements of People with Disabilities

When it comes to creating an accessible kiosk, it's essential to understand the needs of people with disabilities. Knowing what types of disabilities exist, how a disability may impact someone's life, and how people with disabilities interact with technology is key to creating an effective design and user experience. It is also important to differentiate between assistive technology and everyday technology, and to identify common accessibility challenges associated with these two types.

❑ Identifying Different Types of Disabilities

The first step in understanding how to make a kiosk accessible is to identify different types of disabilities. With this knowledge, designers can better tailor their designs to the specific needs of their audience.

Sometimes, disabilities can be categorized by the senses that are affected. Visual, auditory, and mobility disabilities are some of the most common types. Visual disabilities are impairments in the eyes that can range from difficulty seeing color to total blindness. Some visual disabilities include color blindness, retinal damage, glaucoma, nystagmus, and corneal damage. Auditory disabilities are impairments in hearing, such as deafness or partial hearing loss. Mobility disabilities are impairments of the body or neuromuscular system that affect movement and coordination, such as paralysis, cerebral palsy, multiple sclerosis, and spinal cord injuries.

Other disabilities can be grouped by activities that are affected. Psychosocial disabilities are mental health disorders, such as depression, bipolar disorder, and post-traumatic stress disorder. Intellectual disabilities, such as Down syndrome and Autism spectrum disorders, can impede a person's ability to learn, remember, and think. Finally, developmental disabilities include conditions that can cause learning and behavioral difficulties, such as dyslexia, dyscalculia, and language disorder.

❏ Understanding How a Disability can Impact Daily Life

Once designers have identified the types of disabilities, they must understand how those disabilities can affect someone's daily life. This can include physical, cognitive, and communication challenges. Physical challenges can involve difficulty using a computer or typing, difficulty controlling a mouse, and difficulty reading text on a screen. Cognitive challenges may include impaired memory and difficulty processing information. Communication challenges can involve difficulty understanding written words, difficulty speaking, and difficulty understanding spoken words.

❏ Analyzing How People with Disabilities Interact with Technology

People with disabilities may interact with technology in many different ways, such as using keyboard and mouse alternatives, voice commands, and accessibility settings. Keyboard and mouse alternatives are specialized devices that help people with disabilities to use a standard keyboard or mouse. Examples include trackballs, one-handed keyboards, joystick-like devices, and specialized software. Voice commands allow people to control a computer by speaking to it, and accessibility settings can include features such as  screen readers, text enlargers, and screen magnifiers.

❑ Differentiating Between Assistive Technology and Everyday Technology

When creating kiosks for people with disabilities, it's important to understand the differences between assistive technology and everyday technology. Assistive technology is designed to help people with disabilities to perform tasks that may be difficult for them to do with everyday technology. Assistive technology can include items such as wheelchair ramps, audio-assistive devices, and magnifying tools. Everyday technology, on the other hand, is designed to make tasks easier but not to specifically address disability-specific needs.

❑ Examining Common Accessibility Challenges

When creating an accessible kiosk design, it is important to understand the common accessibility challenges that users may encounter. These challenges can include not being able to use the kiosk due to a lack of sufficient instructions, difficulty navigating a website or app due to a lack of contrast or clear labeling, and difficulty interacting with certain components due to their size or placement. It is important to be aware of these issues in order to create an accessible design.

❑ Conclusion

When designing an accessible kiosk, it is important to consider the needs of people with disabilities. Start by identifying different types of disabilities, understanding how a disability can impact daily life, analyzing how people with disabilities interact with technology, differentiating between assistive technology and everyday technology, and examining common accessibility challenges. With this knowledge, designers can create an effective and accessible design for their kiosk.

❑ Understanding Accessibility Regulations and Guidelines

When it comes to kiosks, making sure that people with disabilities can use them is an important part of their design. To ensure this, it's important to understand the regulations and guidelines for accessible kiosks.

Accessibility regulations and laws are put in place to ensure that technology and public spaces can be used by everyone, regardless of disability. Every country has its own laws and regulations, so it's important to familiarize yourself with the laws in your area.

It's also important to look into key resources and reference materials to help you understand the regulations and laws. The World Wide Web Consortium (W3C) is a great online resource for understanding the laws and guidelines. Other helpful resources include the U.S. Access Board and the Department of Justice's ADA Compliance Website.

Adhering to best practices in design is essential to creating an accessible kiosk. Understanding industry standards related to kiosks is essential to meeting these standards. In the U.S., the 2010 ADA Standards for Accessible Design is an important reference guide.

In addition, you should consider the accessibility features that should be included in kiosks. For example, features such as audible and visual cues, voice guidance, larger text, alternative input methods, and adjustable contrast are all important for making a kiosk accessible.

When designing a kiosk, the best way to ensure that it meets accessibility requirements is to familiarize yourself with the latest regulations and laws. It's also important to explore key resources and reference materials, understand the need for best practices in design, explore industry standards related to kiosks, and look at the accessibility features that should be included. With the appropriate knowledge and research, you'll be well on your way to designing an accessible kiosk.

❑ Evaluating the Existing Design of a Kiosk

When assessing the design of an existing kiosk, it is important to understand the needs and requirements of people with disabilities. Identifying different types of disabilities, understanding how a disability can impact daily life, analyzing how people with disabilities interact with technology, and differentiating between assistive technology and everyday technology can help you understand the accessibility challenges of your kiosk.

It is also important to be aware of the regulations and guidelines related to accessibility. Familiarize yourself with the latest accessibility regulations and laws, explore key resources and reference materials, gain an understanding of the need for best practices in design, explore industry standards related to kiosk design, and research what accessibility features should be included in kiosks.

As you evaluate the existing design of the kiosk, look at the components of the kiosk, assess the design to identify needs, and examine the user interface from an accessibility standpoint. Additionally, examine how the kiosk works from a technical perspective to ensure that the current design meets disability needs.

Take into consideration the user experience when designing the kiosk. Consider the context of use for the kiosk, identify the target audience, evaluate how long the updated version of the kiosk should last, examine the current usage patterns, and analyze the current environment for the kiosk.

Choose the appropriate hardware, software, and peripherals for the kiosk. Look at different hardware options, identify the best software to use, find the right types of peripherals, explore various input methods, and examine the types of output devices that should be used.

Finally, analyze ways to make the kiosk easier for people with disabilities to use. Adapt the user interface to improve accessibility, allow the user to customize settings to suit their needs, add features to the user interface that make it easier to use, incorporate voice guidance, text commands and other tools that can improve accessibility, and consider how to make the kiosk easier to use for those with visual, dexterity and cognitive disabilities.

Ultimately, evaluating the existing design of a kiosk is essential to ensure that it meets the needs of people with disabilities. By understanding the requirements of people with disabilities, being aware of the regulations and guidelines, and evaluating the user experience, you can ensure that your kiosk design is an accessible one.

❏ Understanding User Experience in Kiosk Design

When designing a kiosk, it is important to consider the user experience. This consists of understanding the context in which the kiosk will be used, the target audience of the kiosk, and how long the updated version of the kiosk should last. It is essential to examine the current usage patterns for the kiosk and analyze the environment for the kiosk in order to ensure that the design is appropriate for the intended purpose.

24

When considering the context of use, it is important to understand the particular needs of a given location. For example, a kiosk located in an airport may need to accommodate travelers with limited time, while a kiosk located in a museum may need to accommodate visitors who are more interested in leisurely exploration.

It is also important to identify the target audience of the kiosk. Understanding the needs of the target population is essential to producing a successful design. For example, a kiosk intended for use by elders in a retirement community should have an interface that is easy to read and understand, while a kiosk intended for a younger audience should have a more modern and interactive interface.

In addition to understanding the context of use and target audience, it is also important to consider how long the updated version of the kiosk should last. A kiosk that is designed for a temporary location may not need the same level of design consideration as a kiosk intended for a more permanent location.

Examining the current usage patterns for the kiosk is another factor to consider when designing the user experience. Understanding peak times and the specific tasks the kiosk is intended to accomplish can help inform the design process and make sure that the kiosk meets the needs of its users.

Finally, it is important to analyze the environment for the kiosk. This includes assessing the lighting, noise levels, and the size of the space. All of these factors can have an effect on the usability of the kiosk and should be taken into consideration when designing the user experience.

By taking into account the context of use, target audience, and environment of the kiosk, it is possible to design a kiosk that is both accessible and user-friendly. In addition, it is important to consider the usage patterns of the kiosk, the length of time the updated version of the kiosk should last, and the appropriate hardware, software and peripherals for the kiosk. With an understanding of all of these factors, it is possible to create a successful kiosk design that meets the needs of its users.

❑ Choosing the Right Hardware, Software, and Peripherals for Kiosks

Kiosks are powerful tools for providing people with disabilities with access to essential services. But navigating the vast array of available hardware, software, and peripherals can be challenging. The right combination of components can make all the difference when it comes to creating a kiosk that is truly accessible.

When choosing the right hardware, it's important to consider the size and shape of the kiosk. Make sure the kiosk is large enough to fit any assistive technology that may be necessary, such as wheelchair access or other specialized hardware. You should also consider the stability of the kiosk, as well as its weight so that it can be easily moved if needed.

Next, you'll need to choose the right software for your kiosk. Look for software that is compatible with a variety of different operating systems, and that is also accessible to users with disabilities. Specialized software can help to make the kiosk more intuitive for people with disabilities, and can be easily integrated with other hardware and peripherals.

When selecting peripherals, focus on finding devices that are compatible with the kiosk. Look for peripherals that are designed to be accessible, such as large keyboards with Braille characters and voice recognition software. Also, consider choosing peripherals that are easy to use, such as wireless mouse and trackball devices.

Finally, the input and output options of the kiosk are just as important as the hardware and software. For input, look for devices that use standard interfaces, such as USB or Bluetooth. Check that the input devices are compatible with the software and hardware of the kiosk. For output, consider devices such as headphones and large displays to ensure people with vision impairments can still use the kiosk.

By carefully selecting the right hardware, software, and peripherals for the kiosk, you can create a kiosk that is truly accessible. With the right combination of components, you can create a kiosk experience that offers the same level of usability to people with disabilities as it does to those without disabilities.

❑ Making Kiosks Easier to Use for People with Disabilities

Creating a kiosk that is accessible to people with disabilities is an important part of designing technology that works for everyone. That's why it's crucial to take the time to analyze the ways to make kiosks easier for people with disabilities to use.

Adapting the user interface of a kiosk is a great place to start when looking for ways to make it more accessible. Kiosks should have features that make them easier for people with disabilities to navigate, such as larger fonts, better contrast, and clickable elements that can be activated with a single click. Kiosks should also be designed to allow users to customize settings to suit their specific needs, from font sizes and colors to keyboard configurations.

Adding accessibility features to the user interface can also make a big difference. This could include things like incorporating voice guidance into the kiosk's interface and supporting text commands. Voice guidance and text commands can help people with visual impairments more easily interact with the kiosk. Additionally, including an on-screen keyboard could help those with reduced dexterity to use the kiosk.

When looking for ways to make a kiosk more accessible, it's also important to examine the other tools that can be used to improve accessibility. For example, incorporating touchscreens into the kiosk design can make it easier for people with physical challenges or limited mobility to interact with the kiosk. Additionally, incorporating features such as a text-to-speech feature or a voice recognition feature could make the kiosk easier to use for people with hearing impairments.

Finally, it's important to make sure that the kiosk is as easy to use as possible for those with visual impairments. This could include things like increasing the font size of text onscreen, increasing the contrast of text, providing an on-screen magnifier, and utilizing alternative input options such as an enlarged keypad, an on-screen keyboard, or a trackball or joystick.

By taking the time to analyze the ways to make kiosks easier for people with disabilities to use, you can create a kiosk that works for everyone. By adjusting the user interface, providing accessibility features, and examining the accessibility tools available, you can create a kiosk that is accessible to people with disabilities, giving them the freedom to interact with the kiosk in a way that suits their needs.

❑ Conclusion

This chapter provided an overview of how to make kiosks accessible for people with disabilities. In order to ensure that kiosks are accessible, it is important to understand the needs and requirements of people with disabilities and be aware of the various regulations and guidelines related to accessibility. It is also vital to evaluate the existing design of the kiosk and take into consideration the user experience when designing it. Finally, choosing the right hardware, software, and peripheral will help to make kiosks easier for people with disabilities to use.

◤ Learn from Examples of Kiosk Accessibility Implementation

Person 1:

John is a kiosk designer who wants to make it easier for people with disabilities to use his kiosks. He starts by evaluating the existing design of the kiosk and researching the regulations and guidelines. He then chooses hardware like a joystick and a touchpad, and high-contrast fonts and colours for the kiosk interface. He also analyzes ways to make the kiosk easier for people with disabilities to use, like offering spoken-word feedback and automated instructions.

Person 2:

Jess is a kiosk engineer who works to make kiosks accessible to people with disabilities. She begins by understanding the needs of people with disabilities and working out what kind of assistance they may need. She then evaluates the existing design of the kiosk and makes sure it meets the minimum regulations and guidelines. She adds features like a touch-screen interface and adjustable keyboards, so people with disabilities can better interact with the kiosk. She also adds features that make it easier for people with disabilities to use, like tutorials and alternative user controls, like an eye-tracking mouse.

Person 3:

Tim is an accessibility specialist who wants to build kiosks that are user-friendly for people with disabilities. He starts by researching the regulations and guidelines related to accessibility and understanding the requirements of people with disabilities. He then evaluates the existing design of the kiosk and adds features like adjustable volume, high-contrast fonts, and adjustable text size.

He also sets up speech-recognition software and voice-command systems, so people with disabilities can interact with the kiosk in a more efficient way.

## ◣ Step-by-Step Guide to Making Kiosks Accessible

Understand the needs and requirements of people with disabilities
- Research existing and emerging assistive technologies
- Reach out to people with disabilities and ask how they use kiosks
- Learn about the challenges and opportunities of using kiosks

Know the regulations and guidelines related to accessibility
- Familiarize yourself with the WCAG 2.0 standards for accessible web content
- Read the relevant laws, regulations, and guidelines on accessibility
- Review best practices from other countries on accessibility

Evaluate the existing design of a kiosk
- Inspect the current design of the kiosk
- Note down any challenges or limitations in the existing design
- Identify areas that need improvement

Take into consideration user experience when designing the kiosk
- Think about the needs of users with disabilities
- Design an intuitive user interface
- Use colors, text, shapes, and images to create a visually accessible kiosk

Choose the appropriate hardware, software, and peripherals for the kiosk
- Research existing keyboards, touch screens, and pointing devices
- Test the hardware and peripherals for mobility, compatibility, and adjustability
- Identify software programs that support accessibility

Analyze ways to make kiosks easier for people with disabilities to use
- Use access keys and other shortcuts to easily navigate the kiosk

- Make the kiosk audio friendly with sound and auditory cues
- Design the kiosk for the user's comfort, with adjustable viewing angles, ergonomic keyboards, etc.

## ◤ Using a Framework to Make Kiosks Accessible

The E-A-U-H-A Framework:

Evaluate - Analyze - Understand - Hardware - Accessibility

Evaluate the existing design, analyze user experience, understand the needs and requirements of people with disabilities, choose the appropriate hardware, and ensure the kiosk is accessible for all.

## ◤ Common Mistakes to Avoid When Making Kiosks Accessible

One of the most non-obvious things people get wrong when designing kiosks for accessibility is forgetting to consider the needs of the user. Designers often mistakenly think it's enough to just include features that make the kiosk accessible, such as making sure that it has speech recognition capabilities or a larger font size. However, they tend to forget to think about the actual user experience. It is important to ask questions like "How easy is it for the user to interact with the kiosk?" and "Is the kiosk easy to use?"

Another mistake people make is not designing with all disabilities in mind. Designers often forget to consider the needs of people with multiple disabilities, such as visual, hearing, and mobility impairments. It is important to design with all disabilities in mind, as the kiosk needs to work for everyone. Furthermore, some disabilities may not be immediately apparent and it is important to consider those as well, so that the kiosk is truly accessible for everyone.

A third mistake is not understanding the laws and regulations related to accessibility. Different countries and states may have different regulations, so it is important to understand and abide by the laws in the particular jurisdiction where the kiosk is being installed. This includes making sure that the kiosk is compliant with guidelines and standards set forth by organizations such as the Web Accessibility Initiative and the Americans with Disabilities Act.

Lastly, designers may forget to thoroughly test the kiosk for accessibility. It is important to have people with disabilities test the kiosk to ensure that it works as intended. This will help catch any last-minute issues that may have arisen and that can be easily fixed, ensuring that the kiosk is as accessible as possible.

By understanding these mistakes, designers can ensure that they are creating an accessible kiosk that works for everyone. Designers must consider the user experience, design with all disabilities in mind, understand the laws and regulations, and thoroughly test the kiosk. With these considerations, they can ensure that the kiosk is truly accessible and usable by all.

# 3. Assistive Technology and Accessibility

This chapter will explore the importance of assistive technology in creating accessible kiosks. We will look at the different types of assistive technology available and understand the specific needs of users with disabilities. You'll gain knowledge on how to incorporate assistive technology into your kiosk design, as well as discovering the benefits of tailored interface design. We'll also explore the challenges associated with alternative input methods, and understand the importance of testing the kiosk for accessibility. Through this chapter, you will find out how assistive technology can create a positive experience for all users, making your kiosks more accessible and enjoyable.

This story takes place at Emma's school. Emma is a 10-year-old girl who loves to learn, but she has a physical disability that makes it difficult for her to use the regular school computers. At the school, they had installed a kiosk with assistive technology built in to make it easier for Emma to use.

The challenge was that many of the controls were still too difficult for her to use. She tried her best to work with them, but she was often frustrated and it was taking her much longer to do her work than her classmates.

Her parents and teachers worked together to find an alternative input method for Emma. They decided to create a special joystick that would be easier for her to use and would make the kiosk more accessible.

With the help of this new joystick, Emma was able to use the kiosk more easily. She began to finish her work quicker than her classmates and felt confident in her ability to use the kiosk.

This story shows the importance of tailoring kiosk design to make it more accessible to those with disabilities. With the right assistive technology, anyone can access the technology they need to succeed.

❑ Understanding Assistive Technology

Assistive technology (AT) enables people with disabilities to access digital content and use the same products and services as those without disabilities. It helps people perform tasks they would otherwise be unable to do, such as using a computer, typing, using a mouse, or accessing digital content.

There are a variety of types of assistive technology available, ranging from software to hardware. Common examples of software AT include screen readers and voice recognition programs, which can read out loud what is displayed on a computer screen. Hardware AT includes medical devices such as wheelchairs and hand-held controllers.

Using assistive technology can be very beneficial for people with disabilities, as it allows them to interact with computers and digital content more easily. It can make life much more accessible and convenient for individuals who are unable to use conventional input methods, such as a computer mouse or keyboard.

However, there are also several limitations to assistive technology. Cost and availability can be a barrier as some AT can be expensive or difficult to access. User skills are also important, as AT requires some knowledge of how technology works and how to use different programs.

Overall, assistive technology can make digital content and products more accessible and easier to use. It can be a great way to open up new opportunities for people with disabilities and help them take advantage of the same technologies that everyone else can. With the right tools and resources, people with disabilities can access the same content, experience the same products and services, and be on equal footing as people without disabilities.

❏ Gaining Knowledge of the Specific Needs of Users with Disabilities

Having a basic understanding of the different types of disabilities and what they may require in terms of assistive technology (AT) is very important. It is essential to take the time to identify the specific needs of users with disabilities prior to designing a kiosk that is effective and accessible.

❏ Types of Disabilities

The most common types of disabilities include visual impairments, hearing impairments, physical disabilities and cognitive disabilities. Visual impairments can range from partial to total blindness, while hearing impairments can range from partial to total deafness. Physical disabilities can involve anything from limited mobility to paralysis of various body parts, and cognitive disabilities can involve anything from memory loss to difficulty understanding language.

❏ Specific Needs

Users with disabilities often need specific features that make it possible for them to access digital content. Things like navigation aids, text-to-speech, and adjustable font sizes are just some of the features that may be required. It is important to take into consideration the specific needs of the user in order to make sure that the kiosk is as accessible as possible.

❑ Common Barriers

When designing an accessible kiosk, it is important to identify potential barriers that may prevent users with disabilities from accessing the content. Some of the common barriers include text size, font style, color contrast, interface design and more. It is also important to consider how users might interact with the kiosk.

❑ Analyzing User Feedback

In order to gain a better understanding of the specific needs of users with disabilities, it is essential to analyze user feedback. Surveys, interviews, and focus groups are all great ways to gather user feedback. This information can then be used to identify potential solutions that could make kiosks more accessible.

❑ Identifying Potential Solutions

Once a better understanding of the specific needs of users with disabilities has been gained, it is possible to identify potential solutions that can be used to make a kiosk more accessible. Increasing contrast, increasing text size and font style, optimizing interface design and more are all potential solutions that can be used to make a kiosk more accessible. It is important to be mindful of the users' needs when designing a kiosk in order to ensure that it is as accessible as possible.

❑ Integrating Assistive Technology into Kiosk Design

Creating an accessible kiosk that works for all users, regardless of their abilities, is essential. To do this, it's important to make sure that the kiosk is compatible with a range of assistive technology (AT) solutions. This chapter will explore the various guidelines, tips, and tools that can help you ensure that you are incorporating effective AT integration into your design.

When it comes to AT integration, it's important to ensure that the hardware is AT compatible. This means making sure that the hardware can communicate with the AT software and hardware. In addition, you will want to make sure that all of the necessary software is included in the initial design, as well as that it is kept up-to-date. This way, you can ensure that the kiosk works with the latest version of the AT software, without any need for additional updates.

Another important aspect of AT integration is making sure that all the content is accessible to AT users. This includes adding alt-text to all images, ensuring that the text is readable by a screen reader, and ensuring that all HTML tags are properly formatted. Additionally, you should take the time to make sure that all the content is understandable and easy to navigate for users who rely on alternative input methods.

It's also important to keep in mind that you should design your kiosks with universal design principles in mind. This means creating an interface that's easy to use, no matter what kind of abilities a user has. This means making sure that all text is legible and large enough to be seen, creating a menu structure that is simple and clear, and making sure there is enough contrast between the text and the background. Additionally, you should focus on creating an interface that is tailored to the specific needs of users with disabilities. This could include creating customized menus and buttons, or adding larger text to the screen for users with visual impairments.

Finally, it's important to take the time to test your kiosk for accessibility. This means ensuring that keyboard access is available, checking that all content is accessible to AT users, and testing how the kiosk works when used with alternative input methods. You should also consider conducting surveys and interviews with users about their experiences with the kiosk, as well as testing for compliance with disability laws. By taking the time to properly test the kiosk for accessibility, you can ensure that all users can use it comfortably and successfully.

By following these guidelines, you can make sure that you are incorporating effective AT integration into your kiosk design. Not only will this ensure that the kiosk is accessible to all users, but it will also improve the overall user experience by making the kiosk easier to use. Start incorporating AT into your kiosk design today, and you'll be well on your way to creating an accessible, user-friendly kiosk.

❑ Tailored Interface Design

Tailored interface design is a method of creating user interfaces (UIs) that are tailored to the needs of the user by taking into account their abilities and disabilities. This type of design touches on principles of universal design and takes into account not only the various needs of users with disabilities, but also the needs of all users. Tailoring your UI enables you to create a more user-friendly experience and helps you ensure that the kiosk is accessible.

One of the key benefits of tailored interface design is an enhanced user experience. By creating an interface that is tailored specifically to the user and their abilities, you can make the user's experience more intuitive and easier to use. For example, you can create a more visually accessible interface by increasing the contrast between text and background colors. You can also create a more accessible menu structure by creating simple, clear menus that are easy for all users to navigate.

Another benefit of tailored interface design is quick access to content. By creating a menu structure that is tailored to the user's needs and abilities, you can enable them to access the content they need quickly and easily. This is especially important for kiosks as it allows users to quickly find and access the information they need.

When creating a tailored UI, it is important to build on existing universal design principles, such as providing ample contrast between text and background colors and using simple, clear menus. You should also ensure that the interface is compatible with all available assistive technology (AT) solutions, including both hardware and software. This is key to creating an accessible kiosk that can be used by people with disabilities.

Finally, it is important to look at case studies and user feedback when designing tailored interfaces. Looking at existing solutions can provide you with valuable insight into what works and what doesn't. You should also collect feedback from users with disabilities to get their input and make sure the interface is meeting their needs. By incorporating their feedback, you can ensure that your tailored interface is accessible to all users.

Overall, tailored interface design is an important element of kiosk design. By taking into account the needs of all users, you can create a user experience that is tailored specifically to their needs. This can help you create a more accessible and user-friendly kiosk that is accessible to everyone.

Alternative Inputs: Challenges and Opportunities

Alternative input methods offer new and exciting opportunities for making kiosks more accessible to people with disabilities. However, as with any technology, there are challenges associated with using alternative inputs that designers must consider in order to ensure kiosks are accessible.

One of the main challenges with alternative input methods is lack of standardization. Currently, many different alternative input methods exist, but there is no universally accepted standard among them, making it difficult to design kiosks that can cater to a variety of needs. Additionally, many alternative input technologies are still quite new and lack the broad levels of compatibility that other technologies enjoy.

When designing for alternative inputs, usability must be a major consideration. Alternative input methods are often quite difficult to use, and require a high degree of precision and accuracy. Even small changes in the design of an interface can have a major impact on how easy it is to use an alternative input device.

Testing is also an important part of designing for alternative inputs. Focus groups and controlled testing can provide invaluable insight into how easy it is for people with disabilities to use the kiosk. This can reveal potential improvements that can be made to the kiosk design, as well as highlighting any potential barriers to accessibility that may exist.

Finally, successful implementations of alternative input methods often rely on case studies and user feedback. Examples of kiosks that have successfully incorporated alternative input devices can be invaluable in determining which design methods are most effective. Similarly, user feedback and surveys can help to identify how well the kiosk meets the needs of its users.

Overall, alternative inputs offer great potential for making kiosks more accessible, but designers must be aware of the challenges and opportunities associated with them in order to ensure their designs are usable and compliant with disability regulations. With careful planning, testing and attention to detail, kiosks with alternative input methods can offer people with disabilities a more convenient and accessible experience.

❑ Testing for Accessibility: Ensuring Your Kiosk is User-Friendly

Testing for accessibility is an essential part of creating a usable and accessible kiosk. By ensuring your kiosk meets accessibility standards, people with disabilities will have an easier time using it, and your kiosk can be more easily adapted to work with assistive technology.

Accessibility testing should focus on the end user's experience and should include testing for keyboard access, compatibility with assistive technology and features that allow users to adjust text sizes or fonts, for example. During the testing phase, you should look for any areas of the kiosk that might be difficult for people with disabilities to access or use, such as small icons or unfamiliar buttons.

To test for different disabilities, you can create checklists that focus on the specific obstacles people with each disability may face. For example, if your kiosk is designed for people with vision impairment, you can use a checklist to make sure that text size and contrast are set at appropriate levels. Similarly, if your kiosk is designed for people with hearing loss, you can use a checklist to ensure it has features like closed captions and audio descriptions available.

To ensure that your kiosk is compliant with disability laws and regulations, you should take steps to make sure it meets all applicable standards, such as the Americans with Disabilities Act (ADA) and other relevant laws. Additionally, you should keep up-to-date on changes to the laws so you can make any necessary adjustments to your kiosk.

Conducting regular accessibility tests can help you to keep your kiosk up-to-date and compliant with the latest standards. Testing can also help you to identify any areas of the kiosk that need to be improved or updated. For example, you may find that users with disabilities have difficulty understanding a particular interface element or navigating through a particular feature. Making changes to these elements can lead to a better user experience for everyone.

By testing for accessibility and regularly making improvements, you can make sure that your kiosk is always user-friendly for people with disabilities. Doing so will make life easier for those who use the kiosk, and it can also help you to attract more users due to the increased accessibility of your kiosk.

❑ Conclusion

This chapter has explored the use of assistive technology in kiosk design and how it can be used to make kiosks more accessible for people with disabilities. It has discussed the different types of assistive technology available, the needs of the disabled user, and how to incorporate it into interface design. Furthermore, it has highlighted the challenges associated with alternative input methods, as well as the importance of testing the kiosk for accessibility. In conclusion, designing and implementing accessible kiosks is a key step in ensuring that all users can have a positive user experience.


◥ Examples of How Assistive Technology Can Help You

Person 1:

John had a kiosk in his store that needed to be made accessible for wheelchair users. He learned about how changing the height of the kiosk could provide added accessibility and make it easier to use. John made sure to lower the height so that wheelchair users could reach the kiosk without struggling. He also increased the size of the buttons on the kiosk's interface, which allowed users to interact with it more easily.


Person 2:

Jane was working on designing a kiosk for a library. In order to enable access to the kiosk for people with impaired vision, she adopted an interface design approach known as high contrast. This meant that the text was easier to read and the buttons on the kiosk's interface were easier to spot and select. She also implemented voice recognition technology, which allowed users to interact with the kiosk by simply speaking their commands.


Person 3:

Bob wanted to make sure that his kiosk was accessible for people with hearing impairments. He made sure to include a text-to-speech feature in the kiosk's interface, which allowed users to read what was on the screen instead of listening to it. Bob also implemented gesture-based input methods to make it easier for people to interact with the kiosk without having to use a mouse or keyboard. He tested the kiosk to make sure that it was easy to use and that it was able to accommodate all users.

## ◥ Step-by-Step Guide to Accessing Assistive Technology

Understand the Different Types of Assistive Technology Available
- Learn about various assistive technology (AT) devices
- Identify the most commonly used AT devices
- Research how AT devices work and what features are available

Gain Knowledge of the Specific Needs of Users with Disabilities
- Speak to people with disabilities to gain insight into their experiences
- Research the types of challenges they face when using kiosks
- Read reports and studies on the topic

Learn How to Incorporate Assistive Technology Into Kiosk Design
- Study the best practices for integrating AT devices into kiosk design
- Determine how to best utilize the features of various AT devices
- Consider the implications of usability and accessibility

Discover the Benefits of Tailored Interface Design
- Research the benefits of creating an experience tailored to people with disabilities
- Identify the various design options that can be used to make a kiosk accessible
- Make a plan for creating a kiosk interface that meets the needs of all users

Explore the Challenges Associated with Alternative Input Methods
- Understand the different input methods that can be used to interact with a kiosk
- Identify the challenges associated with using alternative input methods
- Learn how to design a kiosk to accommodate all input methods

Understand the Importance of Testing the Kiosk for Accessibility
- Research standards and guidelines for accessibility

- Develop a plan for testing the accessibility of the kiosk
- Conduct tests to ensure the kiosk is accessible to everyone

## ◤ A Step-by-Step Guide to Accessing Assistive Technology - A Useful Framework for You!

The 5 C's Framework:

1. Completion - Ensure usability and completion of tasks for users with disabilities.
2. Connection - Connect users with the appropriate assistive technology.
3. Customize - Tailor the interface to meet the user's needs.
4. Check - Test the kiosk for usability and accessibility.
5. Communications - Establish clear communication paths with users.

## ◤ Common Mistakes to Avoid When Implementing Assistive Technology and Accessibility

It's easy to assume that all kiosk design should be geared towards people with visible disabilities, such as those using wheelchairs or crutches, but this is a mistake. People with invisible disabilities, such as those with hearing, vision, or cognitive impairments, are just as important when it comes to designing accessible kiosks. Many of these individuals may not be immediately visible in crowds, but their needs must still be given priority when designing kiosks for them.

Another common mistake is forgetting about the user experience. Although details such as font size and color may not seem like a priority when designing a kiosk, small changes can make a huge difference in how easy it is for a person with a disability to use the kiosk. Failing to consider the user experience may result in kiosks that are not accessible or difficult to use, forcing people with disabilities to seek alternative methods of accessing the service.

It is also wrong to assume that the only assistive technology available is the one already in use. Technological advancements are constantly being made, which means there are constantly new technologies being developed that can help people with disabilities. It's important to stay informed about the latest assistive technologies and make sure that your kiosk design plans account for them. This can open up a whole new range of possibilities that might not have even been considered before.

Finally, one of the most overlooked mistakes when it comes to kiosk design is the importance of testing. It is impossible to know if a design is truly accessible until it has been tested by people with disabilities. People with disabilities can provide valuable feedback on how the design can be improved, and this feedback should be used to make adjustments before the kiosk is put into use. Failing to test the kiosk can result in kiosks that are ultimately unusable, making it even harder for people with disabilities to access the service they need.

To sum up, designing accessible kiosks is an important way to make sure that everyone can access services equally. People with disabilities should not be forgotten or overlooked when designing kiosks, as their needs are just as important as those of people without disabilities. Furthermore, it is essential to stay informed about the latest assistive technology and to always test the design with users with disabilities to make sure that it works properly. By following these guidelines, accessibility can be enabled through kiosk design.

# 4. Universal Design Principles

In this chapter we will explore the exciting world of universal design and examine how it can be applied to increase accessibility for people with disabilities. We will discuss the seven core principles of universal design and how they can be implemented to make products usable by as many people as possible. We will also discuss how technology can assist people with disabilities and how to determine the appropriate design elements for various disabilities. Finally, we will explore how to analyze the accessibility of existing products and designs. With this comprehensive understanding of universal design, we can unlock the exciting potential of creating an accessible future for everyone.

❑ Understanding Universal Design Principles: Unlocking Accessibility for All.

It was a bright and sunny day in the city when Annika ventured to the mall. She had a mission – to buy a birthday present for her friend. What Annika didn't know is that this outing would challenge her in a way she had never expected.

As she arrived, she noticed something different – a large kiosk with a touchscreen, accessible to those in a wheelchair. Excited, she rolled her wheelchair up to the kiosk, eager to explore all it had to offer. But Annika quickly realized that the kiosk had not been designed with accessibility in mind. She was met with a series of difficulties. The buttons were too small, the text was too small, the contrast wasn't strong enough, and the menus were confusing. All of these issues made it impossible for Annika to use the kiosk.

Frustrated and disappointed, she decided to confront the mall management. After much discussion, the kiosk design was completely revamped. It was now designed with an intuitive layout, larger buttons, larger text, more contrasting colors and more. Annika was overjoyed. For the first time, she could autonomously use a kiosk, with the same ease and convenience as all the other shoppers.

Annika's story is a powerful reminder of the importance of universal design. Kiosks, like other products, must be designed with accessibility in mind, so that everyone – regardless of ability – can use them with ease and convenience.

# Understanding Accessibility and Universal Design

Having accessible products and services means that all people, regardless of their abilities, can use them. Accessibility is the practice of making products and services that are usable by and accessible to the widest variety of people, including those with disabilities, the elderly, and people with different abilities. Accessible products are designed to be usable by as many people as possible.

The concept of accessibility is closely related to universal design. Universal design is a form of design that takes into account the needs of as many people as possible, rather than just designing for a single group of people. Universal design focuses on creating products with inclusive and equitable principles, allowing more people to access and use the product.

The benefits of making products accessible to users with disabilities cannot be understated. By creating products with accessibility in mind, companies can increase their customer base, improve customer satisfaction and loyalty, and demonstrate their commitment to social responsibility. Additionally, many countries have laws that require companies to make their products accessible, and companies can face legal consequences if they do not comply.

Examples of products that are designed with accessibility in mind include low-vision and high-contrast interfaces, voice-recognition software, and screen readers. Assistive technology is a major part of accessibility, as it enables people with disabilities to use a product or service in a manner that is not possible without assistive technology.

It is important to differentiate between accessibility and usability. Accessibility focuses on making products usable by people with disabilities, while usability focuses on making a product easy and intuitive to use for all users, regardless of ability. It is possible to have a product that is accessible, but not usable. For example, a product may be accessible to a blind user, but its user interface may be difficult to use for non-disabled users.

Universal design is a key part of accessibility and an important concept for kiosk designers to understand. By following universal design principles, kiosk designers can create products that are easy to use for everyone, regardless of their age, gender, ability level, or cultural background. In this chapter, we will explore the seven principles of universal design and how they can be applied to kiosk design.

# Recognizing the Seven Design Principles of Universal Design

Universal design is a design process that helps create products, services, and environments that are usable by the widest range of people, regardless of age, ability, or situation. It is based on seven design principles that help create a product or service that can be used by as many people as possible.

The seven design principles of universal design are as follows:

1. Equitable Use: Design for every user, whether disabled or not, to access and use the product with the same level of effort.

2. Flexibility: Design for flexibility and versatility so that the product can be used in different ways.

3. Simple and Intuitive Use: Design the product so that it is simple and easy to use.

4. Perceptible Information: Design the product so that it presents information in a way that users can easily perceive and understand.

5. Tolerance for Error: Design the product so that it can tolerate errors made by users, as well as unexpected actions.

6. Low Physical Effort: Design the product so that it requires a low physical effort to use.

7. Size and Space for Approach and Use: Design the product so that size and space requirements are appropriate for the user.

Using these seven design principles when constructing a new kiosk can help make it as usable as possible for people with disabilities. By recognizing and understanding these design principles, you can create a product that is accessible to the widest range of people. Additionally, it can also lead to numerous other benefits, such as a larger customer base, higher customer satisfaction, and a lower cost of ownership.

❑ Identifying Ways to Make Products Accessible

Making products usable and accessible for as many people as possible is a critical part of designing effective kiosks. In order to do this, it is important to understand user needs and ability levels, as well as customize user experiences and create product accessibility options. Designers should also be aware of how to design for people with physical and cognitive disabilities.

❑ Understanding User Needs and Ability Levels

It is important to consider user needs and ability levels when designing any product or service. Knowing what consumers need to use the product or service, as well as accessibility options they may require, will help inform the design. This can include designing for individuals with visual and hearing impairments, mobility challenges, or cognitive disabilities. It is important to consider the range of abilities when designing products and services, as this will help create a more accessible user experience.

❑ Customizing the User Experience

Customizing the user experience is key to providing an accessible product or service. This can involve adjusting the design of the product or service to meet the needs of the individual user, as well as providing options for users to adjust their own settings for use. For example, a user may need to adjust the font size, color contrast, or layout in order to access the product or service. This can be done through adjustable settings, and is an important part of making a user experience accessible.

❑ Creating Product Accessibility Options

Creating product accessibility options is an important part of making a product or service more accessible to users of all abilities. This can include options such as adjustable font size, color, contrast, and layout. Additionally, creating options that are accessible to people of all cognitive and physical abilities is important. This can include features such as voice recognition technology and screen readers, which can make products more accessible to users with visual or hearing impairments.

❑ Designing for People with Physical and Cognitive Disabilities

Designing for people with physical and cognitive disabilities is an important part of creating an accessible user experience. This can include elements such as large fonts, high contrast colors, alternative text, and options for alternative input devices. Additionally, it is important to consider the accessibility implications of features such as haptic feedback and speech recognition. These features can be appreciated by all users, but may be essential for those with physical or cognitive disabilities.

By considering and understanding user needs, abilities, and accessibility options, designers can create products and services that are accessible to as many people as possible. By doing this, designers can ensure that everyone is able to use and benefit from the product or service.

## Understanding the Use of Assistive Technology

Assistive technology is any system or device that helps people with disabilities to gain access to products, services, or activities that they may not be able to access without it. These technologies range from simple hand-held items to complex electronic devices. Assistive technology provides access to information, communication, and entertainment that can improve the quality of life for people with disabilities.

The type of assistive technology needed is determined by the disability and the activity in which someone wants to participate. Generally, this technology is used to help people with physical, sensory, learning, or cognitive disabilities. For example, voice-recognition software can assist those with physical disabilities by allowing people to enter information into a computer with their voice rather than having to type. Similarly, screen readers can assist those who are visually impaired by reading out the contents of a page or a web page.

The impact of assistive technology on the user experience can be significant. It can provide access to information, communication, and entertainment that would otherwise be impossible. For example, those with physical disabilities can use assistive technology to navigate a website or type out a message on a keyboard. Alternatively, those with sensory disabilities can benefit from assistive technology that provides audio or visual cues that would not be available via traditional means.

Assistive technology can help to bridge the gap between those with disabilities and those without. It can help to create an inclusive, accessible environment that can be accessed by people with a wide range of abilities. This can help to improve the user experience and make it easier for people to access the information they need. In this way, assistive technology can offer a powerful way to ensure that everyone has an equal chance to access the same information.

❑ Determining Design Elements for Disabilities

When designing any product, it is essential to consider the needs of people with disabilities. Design elements such as large fonts, high contrast, and alternative text can go a long way in creating an accessible environment. But how can you determine which specific design elements to use and how to adapt them for different disabilities?

In order to create the most effective and comprehensive design, it is important to first identify the needs of the user. Doing user research, interviewing people with different abilities, and assessing existing design elements can help you understand which design elements are necessary for the project. When designing for people with disabilities, make sure to consider the range of disabilities, such as physical, cognitive, hearing, and visual.

Once the necessary design elements are identified, the next step is to create them. Large fonts, high contrast, and alternative text are design elements that are often used to create accessibility. Large fonts are a great way to make content easier to read for people with low vision or dyslexia. High contrast can make text easier to read for people with low vision and color blindness. Alternative text or "alt-text" is critical for people using screen readers and those who are visually impaired. The alt-text should be descriptive but concise, providing enough information so the user can understand the image or video.

When adapting design elements, you should also consider how the user might interact with the product. For example, if you are designing for people with dexterity challenges, like those with limited movement in their hands, you may need to create larger buttons and text boxes that are easier to click on. For those with cognitive disabilities, you may want to design a user interface with fewer distractions and more obvious navigation. Additionally, you can provide accessibility options such as increasing or decreasing font size or adjusting the brightness.

Finally, it is important to test the accessibility of the product and design. Testing with assistive technology, such as screen readers, can help you identify any potential issues and confirm that the design elements are working properly. Evaluating the usability of the product by getting feedback from users will enable you to fine-tune the design and make any necessary updates.

By understanding the needs of users with disabilities and creating design elements, such as large fonts, high contrast, and alternative text, you can make sure that your product is accessible and usable by as many people as possible. With the right design elements, you can create a more inclusive and accessible experience.

❏ Analyzing Accessibility of Existing Products and Designs

As a designer, you want to make sure that the products and designs you create are accessible to everyone who may use them. To do this, you need to first evaluate the accessibility of your existing products and designs. Here are some tips and tricks to help you get started.

One way to evaluate the accessibility of existing products and designs is to test them with assistive technology. Assistive technology is specialized software and hardware that help people with disabilities interact with computers and other digital devices. Examples of assistive technology include voice-recognition software, screen readers, and adaptive keyboards. By testing your products and designs with assistive technology, you can identify areas where further improvements need to be made.

Another way to evaluate the accessibility of existing products and designs is to evaluate their usability. Usability is the measure of how easily people can interact with and understand an interface. This includes factors such as whether the interface is intuitive, whether users can complete tasks quickly, and whether the interface is accessible to people with different abilities. Evaluating the usability of your existing products and designs is essential for making sure they are accessible to a wide range of users.

Finally, you can use a variety of tips and tricks to improve the accessibility of existing products and designs. Adjusting the text size, utilizing high contrast colors, adding alternative text to images, and making sure every button or link is clickable are all great ways to make existing products and designs more accessible. Additionally, you can consider ways to customize the user experience to meet the needs of various disabilities.

By following these tips and tricks, you can ensure that the products and designs you create are accessible to everyone who may use them. With a little bit of effort and attention to detail, you can easily make sure that your products and designs are accessible and usable by as many people as possible.

❑ Conclusion

This chapter explored the principles of universal design and how technology can help those with disabilities. It examined the seven design principles and identified ways to make products accessible to everyone, regardless of ability. Additionally, it discussed the importance of adapting design elements to meet the needs of people with various disabilities. Finally, it touched on analyzing existing designs for accessibility. Together, these discussions provide an understanding of how universal design can help create a more inclusive world.

❑ Examples of Universal Design in Action: Unlocking Accessibility for You.

1. Maria was designing a new kiosk for a public library. She started by researching the seven principal design elements of universal design and how to make sure her product was usable for as many people as possible. She made sure the kiosk had big buttons and high contrast lettering so that it was easy to read. She also added a joystick control so that the kiosk was accessible to wheelchair users and those with limited dexterity.

2. Jack and his team wanted to create an accessible product. To do that, they needed to understand how technology could assist people with disabilities, and recognize the design elements appropriate for various types of impairments. They added an auditory response system for people with hearing impairments, and ensured the kiosk had a large touchscreen for those with vision impairments.

3. Laura was designing a kiosk for an office building. She wanted to make sure the product was accessible, so she began by looking into the accessibility of existing designs and products. She also looked through blind users' feedback to understand the difficulties they faced while using current products. With this information, she was able to identify features and design elements that would improve the accessibility of the new kiosk. She included voice guidance, and tactile feedback buttons, so that the kiosk was user friendly for all.

## ◥ Step-by-Step Guide to Universal Design Principles for You

Understand accessibility and universal design:

1. Research existing accessibility scenarios and legislation.

2. Identify how various disabilities interact with different types of design.

3. Learn how individuals with disabilities interact with products and services.

Recognize seven design principles of universal design:

1. Identify the seven principles of universal design.

2. Analyze each principle to understand how it can be implemented in practice.

3. Understand the roles of usability, accessibility, and durability within each principle.

Identify ways to make products usable by as many people as possible:

1. Develop product requirements that account for differences in abilities, needs, and preferences.

2. Explore alternative product designs and features.

3. Research recent developments in technology that can enhance usability.

Learn how technology can assist people with disabilities:

1. Research assistive technologies available for people with disabilities.

2. Discuss with experts how people with disabilities are using the latest technology.

3. Understand how the latest technology can be integrated into products to enhance accessibility.

Determine appropriate design elements for various disabilities:

1. Consider individual disabilities and how they interact with product design.

2. Review design guidelines and standards for people with disabilities.

3. Make recommendations on how to incorporate elements that are accessible to people with disabilities.

Analyze the accessibility of existing products and designs:

1. Assess existing products and designs for their level of accessibility.

2. Compare different products and designs to determine how they can be improved.

3. Suggest modifications that will make existing products and designs more accessible.

## ◤ A Useful Framework to Follow for Universal Design Principles

The 3 P's Framework: Plan for Accessibility, Prioritize Universal Design, and Prepare for Different Disabilities.

## ◤ Common Mistakes to Avoid When Applying Universal Design Principles

One of the most common mistakes people make when designing kiosks to be accessible to those with disabilities is not taking into account the various disabilities that may be present. For example, some kiosks are designed for people with vision impairments, but not for those with physical impairments. This is a mistake because a person with a physical impairment may still need to use the kiosk, and it may be impossible for them to do so if it is not designed for them.

Another mistake people make when designing accessible kiosks is not considering the various types of disabilities that may be present. For example, a kiosk designed for those with vision impairments may not be accessible to those with hearing impairments. The kiosk needs to be designed to accommodate both types of disabilities and to provide features that are usable by both groups.

Another common mistake people make when designing kiosks is not considering the layout and design of the kiosk. For example, an accessible kiosk should be designed so that those with physical impairments can easily reach and use all of the features of the kiosk. If the design of the kiosk makes it difficult for someone with a physical impairment to use, then the kiosk is not accessible.

It is also important to consider the amount of time that it takes for people with disabilities to access the kiosk. The kiosk should be designed in such a way that users with disabilities can access it quickly and easily.

Finally, people often overlook the need for testing. An accessible kiosk should be tested on a variety of different users to make sure that it works for everyone. If the kiosk is not tested, it may not be accessible to all users, which would be a mistake.

Designing an accessible kiosk is an important task but it is not always easy. People make mistakes when designing kiosks, such as not taking into account the various disabilities that may be present, neglecting to consider the layout and design of the kiosk, and overlooking the need for testing. It is important to address these mistakes in order to ensure that the kiosk is accessible to all users.

## 5. Creating User-Friendly Interfaces

Are you looking for an effective way to create an interface that is both user-friendly and accessible? In this chapter, we will discuss how to design a user-friendly interface that will make it easy and enjoyable for users to navigate your kiosk. We'll explore techniques for choosing the right colors, sizes, fonts, and icons, as well as developing quick and easy navigation methods. Where appropriate, we'll also discuss how to ensure interface elements are correctly labeled and understandable. By the end of this chapter, you will have a better understanding of how to create user-friendly and accessible kiosk interfaces.

◥ Creating User-Friendly Interfaces: Unlocking the Power of Accessibility for You and Your Users

In a small rural community, there was an elderly man who used a wheelchair to get around. He had wanted to use the local library to do some research, but he soon discovered that the entrance to the library was blocked off with a step. He admired the beautiful building and wanted to use the services, but he was unable to access the library due to the step.

He approached the city council and pleaded with them to create a user-friendly interface for the library by installing a wheelchair ramp. The people of the city were skeptical and believed that it would be too expensive and complicated to install. But the man persisted and eventually the city council agreed to install the ramp.

When the ramp was completed, the elderly man in the wheelchair had tears of joy in his eyes. The ramp enabled him to access the library and get the research he wanted. The ramp was a simple solution to a complex problem, and its installation demonstrated the importance of creating user-friendly interfaces.

❑ Creating User-Friendly Interfaces

Designing a user interface that is easy to navigate is essential for providing a smooth and enjoyable experience for users. Making the user journey as simple and efficient as possible will ensure that users are able to complete tasks quickly and without difficulty. Here are some tips for designing user-friendly interfaces:

❑ Streamlining the User Journey:
Streamlining the user journey involves reducing the number of steps needed to complete a task, minimizing the need for scrolling, and other factors to make the user journey as efficient as possible. This includes designing a layout that allows the user to move easily from one item to the next, intuitive placement of navigation elements, and creating a consistent user interface. It's important to consider how the user journey will affect the overall usability and accessibility of the interface as well.

❑ Optimizing the Placement of Elements:

Where you place your elements can have a huge impact on the overall user experience. It's important to position important elements within easy reach, ensure the relevant elements are visible, and optimize the placement of elements for accessibility purposes. For example, when designing for visually impaired people, the user interface should be designed to provide clear cues and landmarks to make them easier to find. In addition, elements should be well spaced out and organized so that users can easily move between them.

❑ Usability Testing:

Usability testing is an important part of designing user-friendly interfaces. This involves testing the interface with target users and evaluating the effectiveness of design elements. Usability testing can help identify any potential issues and areas for improvement. It's important to involve the user in the usability testing process, as their feedback can be invaluable when it comes to making sure the user interface is working as it should.

❑ Making Sure the User Experience is Seamless:

The user experience should be as seamless as possible, with no distractions or unnecessary pop-ups. To ensure a seamless experience, it's important to make sure all elements are optimized for speed and responsiveness. All buttons, links, and other interactive elements should be easy to find and understand, and the loading time should be minimized. In addition, the interface should be designed to be visually pleasing and inviting for users.

By following these tips, you can design an interface that is easy for users to navigate. Streamlining the user journey, optimizing the placement of elements, usability testing, and making sure the user experience is seamless are all key aspects of creating user-friendly interfaces. By focusing on these areas, you can create an interface that enhances accessibility and provides a smooth and enjoyable user experience.

❑ Creating an Intuitive Layout and Design Elements

When it comes to creating a kiosk that is accessible for all users, an intuitive layout and design elements must be considered carefully. By taking the time to understand the principles of universal design, create user-friendly interfaces and understand the intersection of technology and disability, you can create kiosks that empower people with disabilities.

❑ Utilizing the Correct Measurements

When it comes to creating a user-friendly interface, one of the most important aspects is to use the correct measurements. This means that the elements in the design should all use standard measurements, making sure that the elements are correctly spaced and easily reachable. This will ensure a consistent and familiar user experience, making it easier for people of all abilities to access and use the kiosk.

❑ Designing a Consistent Layout

The layout of the kiosk should also be consistent, with the elements placed in the same location consistently. This will ensure an intuitive user journey, with a logical flow of the design that makes it easy to use. Having a consistent layout and design will also make it easier for people with disabilities to use and understand the design, providing a more inclusive experience.

❑ Leveraging the Power of Color

The power of color should also be utilized when creating a user-friendly interface. This means creating a balanced palette, choosing the right colors for different elements and creating a visually appealing design. It is important to remember that some people may be colorblind, so the color choices should take this into account to ensure that every user can enjoy the same experience.

❑ Utilizing the Appropriate Types of Font

Finally, the appropriate types of font need to be used in the design. This means determining which font types work best, picking the right font size and weight and ensuring that the font is not too small or difficult to read. Different font types can have a dramatic impact on the accessibility of the kiosk, so it is important to make sure that the font chosen is appropriate and readable for everyone.

❑ Choosing the Right Colors, Sizes and Font for Elements

When creating user-friendly interfaces for kiosks, color, size and font are all key elements that must be taken into consideration. Utilizing the power of color is essential to creating a balanced and appealing aesthetic, while also ensuring that users can easily distinguish between different elements. Identifying the best sizes for elements is also important, as making sure elements are legible and easy to read is essential for achieving a successful interface. Finally, selecting the right font type, weight and size is also essential for creating an interface that is readable and understandable.

When using color, it is important that kiosk designers create a balanced palette that allows users to easily distinguish between different elements. For example, a color palette of two or three colors can help to make the interface more engaging, while also making it easier to understand the flow of information. Additionally, designers should also carefully select the right colors for different elements, such as avoiding very bright or dark colors when designing buttons, as this can make them difficult to read.

The size of elements is also important when creating user-friendly interfaces for kiosks. Elements must be sized correctly for optimal legibility, and designers should also take into consideration the type of element when choosing the best size. For example, buttons should be large enough so that they are easily clickable, while text should be small enough to read without straining the eyes. Additionally, designers should also make sure that elements are correctly spaced in order to minimize confusion, with the correct measurements ensuring that everything looks aesthetically pleasing.

Finally, font type, weight and size all contribute to legibility, and selecting the right font is essential for creating an interface that is both readable and understandable. In terms of font type, designers should look for fonts that are clean and easy to read, with clear letterforms that are also aesthetically pleasing. Additionally, for buttons and other interactive elements, designers should also choose a font weight that stands out, making these elements easier to identify. Finally, designers should also pay attention to the font size, making sure that it is legible without being too small or too large.

By taking into consideration color, size and font when designing user-friendly interfaces, kiosk designers can create an interface that is easy and enjoyable to use. By carefully selecting the right colors, sizes and fonts, designers can ensure that their kiosk designs are both visually appealing and accessible to all users.

❏ Using Appropriate Imagery and Icons

When designing a user-friendly kiosk, selecting the right type of imagery and icons is essential. Adding the appropriate visuals to your interface will help create a user experience that is easy to navigate.

When selecting images, be sure that they are relevant to the design and high-quality. Having images that are low-resolution or out-of-place can negatively impact the user's experience. It is also important to ensure that the images are appropriate and follow any copyright laws.

Icons can be used to clearly differentiate between different sections in a kiosk, as well as to help guide the user journey. Selecting the right symbols is critical; an icon with the wrong message can create confusion and make the kiosk less user-friendly. Make sure that the icons are easily recognizable, no matter where the kiosk is being used.

It is important to find the perfect balance with visuals. Too many images, icons, and other elements can result in an overcrowded interface, which can be difficult for the user to navigate. Conversely, having too few elements can leave the kiosk feeling sparse and make it hard for the user to find what they're looking for.

In addition to finding the right balance, it is important to make sure that no elements are too overwhelming. Subdued colors, subtle icon shapes, and smaller font sizes can help create a more calming experience for the user.

Finally, it is important to consider how the visuals will fit within the context of the kiosk. Elements like contrast or visual hierarchy should be closely examined to ensure that the placement of the elements is logical and that important information is easy to find.

By selecting the appropriate imagery and icons and creating a well-balanced layout, a kiosk will be easier and more enjoyable to use. Utilizing the right visuals can help create an interface that is intuitive and user-friendly.

❏  Navigating the Kiosk: Quick and Easy

Creating a user-friendly interface for a kiosk involves identifying the best type of navigation, crafting a clear hierarchy, creating a search bar, and implementing a "back" button. All of these elements will help users move through the kiosk quickly and easily.

Choosing the best type of navigation is essential to make the user experience easy and efficient. It is important to consider the different ways a user might interact with the kiosk, including scrolling, swiping, tapping, and clicking. When determining the best type of navigation, it is important to consider the kiosk's interface, the level of complexity, and the types of user inputs.

Once you have determined the best type of navigation, the next step is to craft a clear hierarchy. This involves placing elements in the same location consistently, maintaining a logical flow of the design, and grouping similar elements together. This will help ensure that users can easily find the information they're looking for and move through the kiosk without confusion.

Another important element of creating a user-friendly interface is creating a search bar. This allows users to locate information quickly and easily. It should be clearly labelled and highly functional. Additionally, it is important to make sure that the search function is adjustable so that users can refine their search and receive more accurate results.

The final element to consider when creating a user-friendly navigation system is implementing a "back" button. This will allow users to go back to the previous screen quickly and easily. The "back" button should be easily visible and work without any glitches. Additionally, it should be accompanied by a "forward" button so users can move forward as well.

By following these steps, it is possible to create a kiosk interface that is easy to navigate and user-friendly. The key is to make sure that the elements are clearly labelled and placed in an intuitive layout. Additionally, it is important to create a search bar and "back" and "forward" buttons to make sure users have the necessary tools to quickly and easily move through the kiosk. With these simple steps, you'll be well on your way to creating a user-friendly interface for your kiosk.

❑ Labelling Your Interface Elements: Creating a User-Friendly Experience

When designing a kiosk, it is important to create an interface that is simple to use, clear and intuitive. This means making sure that all elements of the interface are appropriately labelled and easy to understand. Labelling your interface correctly not only makes it easier for people with disabilities to use, but will also make it easier for all users to interact with the kiosk.

❑ Choosing the Right Labels

The first step is selecting the right labels for your interface elements. Labels should be easy to understand and should not contain obscure terms. The labels should be clearly visible, and should give users an idea of what is expected of them when interacting with the kiosk. In addition, you should avoid the use of symbols or acronyms that could be confused with other elements.

❑ Creating Helpful Descriptions

It is also important to provide helpful descriptions for each element. This should include information about what the element is for, how it functions, and what type of input is expected. Descriptions should be written in plain language, so that all users can understand them. The descriptions should also be tailored to the different levels of user understanding, so that all users can access the kiosk without difficulty.

❑ Utilizing Inactive Elements

Inactive elements can be helpful in guiding users. These elements should be clearly labelled, so that users can easily identify their purpose. For instance, if a button is inactive, it should be labelled as such. This avoids confusion, and prevents users from clicking on elements that are not meant to be interacted with.

❑ Using Appropriate Graphics

Graphics can also be used to enliven the interface and to help guide users. When selecting graphics, it is important to make sure that they are relevant to the design. They should also be of high quality, and must be clearly visible. This is especially important for users with visual impairments, who might rely more heavily on these visuals to understand the kiosk.

By labelling your interface elements correctly and providing helpful descriptions, you can create an accessible and user-friendly kiosk experience for all. This will ensure that anyone can access the kiosk and complete their tasks with ease.

❏ Conclusion

The chapter concluded that creating a user-friendly and intuitive interface is essential for a successful product. Designers must carefully consider the layout, color, font, imagery, and navigation when designing an interface. If done right, an interface can be a great tool to help users interact with a product easier and faster. With the right design, a user can quickly and easily navigate the product and make the most of it.

◤ Examples of Accessibility Implementation for You and Your Users

Person 1: Matthew designed an interface for an ATM machine that would allow people with disabilities to easily withdraw money. He included large buttons with a clear font, and added a keypad with oversized keys. He also included an illuminated array of icons at the bottom of the screen to help users quickly find the feature they need.

Person 2: Jennifer created a kiosk for ordering food from a restaurant. She used a large font size and clear labels for each button, and added a large 'Confirm' button at the bottom of the screen. She also included an audio prompt feature that would read out the user's order after it was selected.

Person 3: Nick designed a touch screen kiosk for a museum. He chose bright colors for the different sections on the screen - green for navigation, blue for information and red for video. He also added an audio guide feature to help users find their way around the museum.

❑ Creating User-Friendly Interfaces:

Stage 1: Designing an interface that is easy for users to navigate

- Brainstorm ideas on how to best enable navigation

- Sketch a few initial design ideas

- Choose one design and iterate on it

Stage 2: Creating an intuitive layout and design elements

- Brainstorm different types of design elements

- Choose the best design elements for your design

- Select the size, color, and font of the elements

Stage 3: Choosing the right color, size, and font for elements

- Determine the best color for the interface

- Select the right size for each element

- Find a font that is easy to read

Stage 4: Using appropriate imagery and icons

- Brainstorm ideas for images and icons

- Select the best images and icons for the design

- Make sure they are relevant to the design

Stage 5: Developing quick and easy navigation methods

- Determine the quickest path to navigate the interface

- Sketch out additional navigation methods

- Select the appropriate navigation method

Stage 6: Making sure interface elements are correctly labeled and understandable

- Write labels for all interface elements

- Design labels that are easy to follow

- Review all labels to make sure they are understandable

◥ Strategize Your Accessibility Implementation with a Helpful Framework

❑ The F.A.S.T Formula:

•Flexibility: Design an interface that allows users to navigate in different ways.

•Accessibility: Choose color, size, font, and other elements that are accessible to all.

•Simplicity: Keep the interface simple and clean.

•Testing: Make sure interface elements are clearly and correctly labeled and easy to understand.

◥ Avoiding Common Mistakes in Designing User-Friendly Interfaces

Many people make the mistake of assuming that the way they use technology is the same way everyone else does. But this is not always the case when it comes to designing kiosks for people with disabilities. It's important to understand that the needs of people with disabilities can vary widely and that the way they interact with technology might be vastly different from how most other people do.

One non-obvious mistake people often make is not taking into account the range of disabilities that people might have. For example, some people with disabilities might rely more heavily on sound, tactile response, or visual cues than others. It's important to design kiosks that can accommodate these needs and provide a variety of options for interacting with the kiosk.

Another mistake is not planning for possible conflicts that could arise between the user and the kiosk. For example, some people with disabilities may not be able to interact with the kiosk through traditional touchscreen or keyboard methods. The kiosk should be designed to provide alternative methods of interaction, such as tactile response, voice recognition, or specialized buttons or switches.

It's also important to be aware of potential cognitive issues that could affect how users interact with the kiosk. People with cognitive impairments might find it difficult to remember things such as commands or menus, and might not understand the layout of the kiosk. It's important to consider these issues when designing the kiosk interface, and to provide clear and consistent labels and instructions.

Lastly, many people wrongly assume that the design of a kiosk doesn't matter for people with disabilities. But the design of a kiosk is actually very important. Not only should the kiosk be designed to be accessible, it should also be designed to be intuitive and user-friendly. Poor design can cause confusion and frustration, leading users to turn away from the kiosk. Accessibility should be a priority when designing kiosks, and often involves making smaller changes such as increasing the size of buttons or increasing the space between elements.

In conclusion, there are many non-obvious mistakes that people make when designing kiosks for people with disabilities. It's important to be aware of the needs of users with different disabilities, to plan for potential conflicts between the user and the kiosk, and to carefully consider the design of the kiosk. When these issues are taken into account, users will be able to interact with the kiosk more easily and effectively.

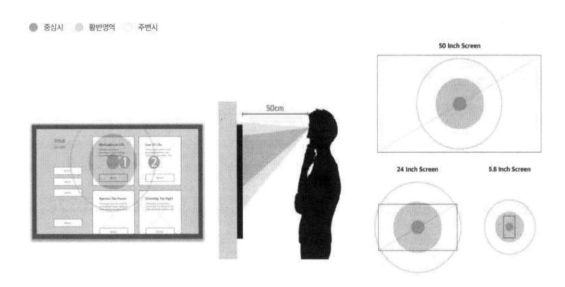

Source. Age-Friendly Digital Accessibility Standards, https://smart.seoul.go.kr

# 6. Understanding the Accessibility Impact of Your Design

This chapter is focused on understanding the accessibility impact of your design, and how to optimize a kiosk for maximum accessibility. Here, you'll learn the importance of understanding the context of user needs, as well as how accessibility principles are related to design. You will gain insight into the functional requirements of users with disabilities and how to increase accessibility by evaluating existing design decisions. You'll also be made aware of assistive technologies and how to recognize and avoid potential user experience issues related to accessibility. By reading this chapter, you'll be able to further create a user-friendly and accessible kiosk with ease.

◥ Why Understanding the Accessibility Impact of Your Design is Important for Everyone

It was a cold, grey winter day in the small town of Meadowdale. In the middle of town stood a community recreation centre. At the entrance of the centre was a kiosk. It was an obstacle for Tanya, a high school student with cerebral palsy. Tanya had to use a wheelchair to get around, making it difficult to access the kiosk. She consulted with the kiosk designer and, together, they came up with a plan to make the kiosk more accessible. They added a voice command feature, adjustable angles, and larger touchscreens so that everyone could use the kiosk, regardless of their disability. With the new features in place, Tanya was finally able to access the kiosk without any trouble. The new design of the kiosk gave Tanya—and all members of the community—the dignified autonomy they deserved.

❑ Understanding User Needs

It is crucial to understand the user needs in order to make sure the kiosk design is accessible to all, including people with disabilities. Identifying the target audience, defining user goals, analyzing user demographics, evaluating user feedback, understanding the user environment, and researching user challenges all play important roles in this.

Identifying the target audience is essential as it helps to shape the design of the kiosk. Knowing who will use the kiosk will help to determine the accessibility needs of the intended audience and how best to meet them. For example, if the kiosk is intended for people with a range of physical and cognitive disabilities, the design must take those needs into account.

Defining user goals is also important as it can help to guide the design of the kiosk. If the goal is usability, then the design needs to consider features such as clear labels, easy-to-use buttons, and immediate feedback. On the other hand, if the goal is efficiency, then the design needs to take into account features such as automation and fast response times.

Analyzing user demographics and evaluating user feedback can provide valuable insights for the design of the kiosk. Knowing the demographic characteristics of the target audience can help to ensure that the kiosk design is appropriate for their needs. Evaluating user feedback can provide an understanding of what the users need and expect from the kiosk, so that those needs can be taken into account when designing the kiosk.

Understanding the user environment is also important, as the design must take into account the unique layout and characteristics of the environment in which the kiosk will be used. For example, if the kiosk is being placed in a noisy area, then the design should include features such as increased volume or noise reduction. If the kiosk is being placed in a cramped space, then the design should include features such as controllable size and height.

Finally, researching user challenges is essential in order to address any potential accessibility issues. Through research, one can identify potential challenges, determine the best solutions, and create a kiosk design that takes into account user needs and expectations. This can help to ensure that the kiosk is as accessible and user-friendly as possible.

❑ Understanding Design Principles

Designing with accessibility in mind is essential if we want to make sure that all users, especially those with disabilities, can use our kiosks. This means understanding the principles of universal design, which are the basic guidelines for making products, services, and environments that are accessible to all people, regardless of age, size, or ability.

The most basic universal design principle is that the design should be simple and intuitive, so that it can be used by anyone. This means avoiding unnecessary features or buttons that might confuse the user. This also means making sure that the kiosk design fits the context of its environment, so that it is easy to use.

Another important principle to keep in mind is that the design should be user-friendly, meaning that it should be comfortable to use and make the user's experience easier. This can include making sure that the interface is intuitive for users to navigate, and that the design is comfortable to use for people with limited dexterity or vision.

When it comes to identifying common challenges related to accessibility, it is important to consider how disabled people interact with technology. For example, people with limited mobility may have difficulty using a standard keyboard, while people with vision impairment may need larger text sizes or alternative input methods. It is also important to consider how people with disabilities use the kiosks, such as providing audio cues or enlarged buttons.

Finally, making design decisions that are beneficial for users with disabilities means recognizing the assistance that assistive technologies can provide. For example, speech recognition can help people with limited mobility interact with the kiosk, while audio cues can help people with vision impairments more easily interact with the interface. It is also important to make sure that the design can accommodate alternative input methods, such as keyboards that use large buttons or voice commands.

By considering the principles of universal design, identifying common challenges related to accessibility, and understanding the functional requirements of users with disabilities, you can create kiosks that are easy and comfortable to use. By making design decisions that are beneficial for users with disabilities and taking into account the assistance that assistive technologies can provide, you can ensure that your kiosks are as accessible as possible.

❑ Understanding the Functional Requirements of Users with Disabilities

When it comes to accessibility, it's important to understand the functional requirements of users with disabilities. It's essential to be aware of their needs and the technology that exists to help them. This will help you design a kiosk that meets the needs of those with disabilities.

The first step in assessing user needs is to identify the target user. This includes gaining an understanding of the demographic information and user goals. You'll also want to analyze user feedback and make sure you understand the user environment. Researching user challenges can also provide valuable insights.

Once you have identified the target user, you can begin to explore the principles of universal design. This includes learning how to apply these principles to different designs. It's also important to identify any common challenges associated with accessibility. This can inform design decisions to make sure that the kiosk is beneficial for users with disabilities.

When assessing the user needs, it's important to explore alternative technologies. This can include determining the optimal solutions for users with disabilities. It's also essential to understand the limitations of certain technologies. For example, some technologies may not be as accessible as others, so it's important to weigh this up when choosing what to use.

To increase accessibility, it's also important to evaluate existing design decisions. This includes examining existing designs, identifying and eliminating design flaws, testing usability with different disabilities and assessing the impact of design decisions on user experience.

Finally, when designing a kiosk for users with disabilities, you'll need to be aware of assistive technologies. This includes exploring the most commonly used assistive technologies and understanding their capabilities. It's also important to evaluate the impact of using alternative technologies, as well as understanding the implications of using alternative technologies.

Furthermore, you should recognize and avoid potential user experience issues related to accessibility. This includes analyzing user feedback, identifying common usability flaws and assessing the impact of design decisions on user experience. It's also important to understand the limitations of certain technologies, avoid common user experience mistakes, and optimize designs for accessibility.

By following these steps, you can design a kiosk that is accessible and beneficial for users with disabilities. Understanding the functional requirements of users with disabilities is the key to designing an effective kiosk that meets the needs of those with disabilities.

❑ Understanding Design Decisions for Accessibility

When designing kiosks, it is important to consider how it may be used by people with disabilities. This means evaluating the impact of design decisions on user experience and proactively avoiding any potential user experience issues. By examining existing designs, testing usability with different disabilities, and understanding the implications of using alternative technologies, you'll be able to make informed adjustments to your designs that will create a more accessible experience for all users.

❑ Examining Existing Designs

The first step in ensuring accessibility through kiosk design is to examine existing designs. Consider the ways they may be used, what elements might be difficult for someone with a disability to interact with, and what could be improved. Pay attention to details such as the size of the buttons, touchscreens, readability of fonts and text, accessibility of images, and more. Make sure to also take into account different disabilities and how they could affect how a user interacts with the kiosk.

❑ Identifying and Eliminating Design Flaws

After examining existing designs, the next step is to identify and eliminate any design flaws that may make it difficult for someone with a disability to use the kiosk. This includes anything from accessibility issues with the user interface to usability issues with the buttons or touchscreens. Pay attention to details such as font size, text readability, size of elements, and more. Consider what changes you can make to create a more accessible experience for all users.

❑ Testing Usability with Different Disabilities

It is also important to test the usability of the kiosk with different disabilities. This could include testing the accessibility of the user interface, the size and number of buttons, readability of the text, and more. Pay attention to how people with different disabilities interact with the kiosk, and consider any improvements that can be made. Make sure to also take into account the different assistive technologies that may be used and how these could affect the user experience.

❑ Assessing the Impact of Design Decisions on User Experience

Finally, it is important to assess the impact of design decisions on user experience. This could range from evaluating the size and number of buttons, to readability of the text, and more. Consider how the design decisions may affect the user's ability to interact with the kiosk. Make sure to also take into account the different disabilities that could be present and how they could affect the user experience. Think about the changes you can make to create a more accessible experience for all users.

❑ Understanding Assistive Technologies

In this section, we'll look at the different types of assistive technologies and how they can be used to make kiosks more accessible for people with disabilities. Assistive technologies are tools and technologies that help people with disabilities interact with computers, the internet and other assistive devices, making life easier for them.

The most commonly used assistive technologies include screen readers, speech recognition systems, keyboard commands and alternative input devices, such as switches and pointing devices. Screen readers are programs that allow people with visual impairments to access and use computer applications and the internet. Speech recognition systems also help people with visual impairments by allowing them to control their computers using voice commands. Keyboard commands and alternative input devices are designed to aid people who may not be able to use a regular computer keyboard or mouse, such as those with physical or dexterity impairments.

When designing a kiosk, it is important to understand the capabilities of the different assistive technologies and how they can be used to make the experience easier and more accessible for users with disabilities. For example, a kiosk designed for people with visual impairments should include a screen reader, and a kiosk designed for people with physical or dexterity impairments should include alternative input devices, such as switches and pointing devices. It is also important to understand the implications of using different types of assistive technologies, such as the cost associated with purchasing and maintaining the technology, as well as the potential impact on usability.

When designing a kiosk, it is important to take into account the needs of users with disabilities and ensure that they are able to access and use the kiosk without any impediments. To do this, designers should research different assistive technologies, understand their capabilities and limitations, and use the appropriate technologies in their designs. This will help to ensure that users with disabilities are able to use the kiosk effectively and have a positive experience.

❑ Recognizing and Avoiding User Experience Issues

When designing a kiosk, it is necessary to think deeply about how the design will impact the user experience. Accessibility considerations should always be top of mind, as it is essential to understand the user challenges associated with certain disabilities. Analyzing user feedback, identifying common usability flaws, and assessing the impact of design decisions on user experience can help ensure that a kiosk is optimized for accessibility.

In order to understand potential user experience issues, it is important to be aware of the different types of assistive technologies that can be used for users with disabilities. Exploring the most commonly used assistive technologies, and researching their capabilities, will give the designer an understanding of the different solutions that can be implemented. Additionally, researching the implications of using alternative technologies can be useful in order to determine the optimal solutions for users with disabilities.

Another important consideration is to be aware of the potential user experience issues that can arise from poor design decisions. For example, a common mistake when designing for accessibility is to ignore the needs of users with disabilities and limit access to certain features. It is important to identify design flaws, such as the lack of accessibility options, and to test usability with different disabilities. It is also necessary to assess the impact of design decisions on user experience and to understand the limitations of certain technologies.

Once the user experience issues are understood, it is possible to apply the principles of universal design to optimize the design for accessibility. Universal design is an approach to designing products, environments and services that can be used by all people, regardless of their abilities. By learning how to apply the principles of universal design to different designs, it is possible to create user-friendly interfaces that are beneficial for users with disabilities.

Finally, it is important to be aware of the potential user experience issues related to accessibility and take steps to avoid them. By analyzing user feedback, identifying common usability flaws, and assessing the impact of design decisions on user experience, it is possible to identify and eliminate design flaws that could potentially hinder a user's experience. Additionally, understanding the implications of using alternative technologies, as well as avoiding common user experience mistakes, can help to ensure that the design is optimized for accessibility.

## Summary

This chapter explored the impact of design decisions on accessibility. We discussed the importance of understanding user needs, how accessibility principles are related to design, how to evaluate existing design decisions, and the need to be aware of assistive technologies. We also looked at how to recognize and avoid potential user experience issues related to accessibility. By taking the time to consider the accessibility impact of design decisions, developers can ensure that their products are usable and accessible to all users.

◥ Examples That Show How Accessibility Impacts Us All

Person 1: Anna was a web designer who was creating a new online store. She wanted to make sure that it was as accessible as possible, so she made sure that her website included features like accessible fonts, colour contrast, adjustable font sizes, and clickable elements that were large enough for users with poor motor control to click on easily.

Person 2: Robert was a product designer for a kiosk company. He was designing a new kiosk for use in a public setting and wanted to ensure that the kiosk was accessible for people with disabilities. He designed a kiosk that included a lowered display screen for wheelchair users, a voice recognition system for users with visual impairments, and a tactile keyboard for users with motor skills issues.

Person 3: Megan was tasked with designing a touchscreen application for public use in a government office. She wanted to ensure that the application was usable by everyone, so she included an on-screen keyboard that was large enough for users with visual impairments to see, an audio description option to provide audio feedback for the user, and an interface that was easy to use for users with limited mobility.

■ Step-by-Step List: Examples of Accessibility Impacts in Our Lives


Stage 1: Understanding the Context of User Needs

- Research the needs of users with disabilities that could be using the kiosk

- Gain a deeper understanding of the impact of disability on user experience

- Consider the unique needs of different types of disabilities when creating the kiosk design


Stage 2: How Accessibility Principles are Related to Design

- Identify the accessibility principles that best fit the kiosk design

- Incorporate accessibility principles into the design to ensure it is suitable for users with disabilities

- Assess the design to ensure it meets the universal design needs


Stage 3: Understanding the Functional Requirements of Users with Disabilities

- Consider what type of assistive technology users with disabilities might need

- Identify the functional requirements of users with disabilities

- Incorporate the requirements into the design of the kiosk


Stage 4: Ways to Increase Accessibility by Evaluating Existing Design Decisions

- Evaluate existing design decisions to determine what elements can be improved to make the kiosk more accessible

- Look for potential design issues that could be obstacles to user accessibility

- Make necessary changes to the design based on the evaluation


Stage 5: The Need to be Aware of Assistive Technologies

- Gain knowledge on the types of assistive technology available

- Research the compatibility of assistive technologies with the kiosk design

- Make sure to build a design that is compatible with all types of assistive technology


Stage 6: Recognizing and Avoiding Potential User Experience Issues Related to Accessibility

- Conduct user tests with people with disabilities to identify any potential user experience issues related to accessibility

- Make changes to the design to address any issues found

‒ Make sure to test the design after making changes to ensure that any accessibility problems have been resolved.

### ◥ "Identifying Accessibility Impacts: A Useful Framework for You"

The ADA Accessibility Action Framework:

A. Assess: Review existing design decisions and understand the functional requirements of users with disabilities.

B. Design: Incorporate universal design principles and user-friendly interfaces.

C. Assist: Research assistive technologies that can further increase accessibility.

D. Avoid: Identify and address potential user experience issues related to accessibility.

### ◥ Common Mistakes to Avoid When Designing for Accessibility

One of the most common mistakes people make when designing kiosks for people with disabilities is equating accessibility with usability. While accessibility focuses on creating an experience that is easy to understand and use for all people, usability is more about the overall efficiency and effectiveness of the experience. Without a focus on usability, it's easy to overlook some of the factors that make kiosks easier to use, such as readability of text, the ability to quickly find what you need, and how quickly the kiosk responds to commands.

Another mistake people often make is assuming that all accessibility features are one-size-fits-all. While some features are designed to work for all disabilities, there's actually a lot to consider when designing accessible kiosks. For instance, people who are blind need to be able to receive spoken instructions, while those

who are deaf require visual cues. People in wheelchairs may need to be able to access the kiosk from different heights or angles. By understanding the specific needs of a given population, it's possible to design a kiosk experience that is tailored to that audience.

Another mistake people make is not putting enough focus on the user experience. A kiosk designed with accessibility in mind won't be useful if users don't understand how to interact with it. Accessible design should focus on creating an intuitive experience that users can easily navigate and understand. This includes considering the visual design of the kiosk, making sure the text is large enough to read, and ensuring that all buttons are easy to locate and press. While accessibility is important, usability should be a top priority.

Lastly, people often forget to test their kiosks for accessibility. While the design process may include considering how people with disabilities are likely to interact with the kiosk, it's important to involve actual users to make sure the design is successful. Testing with real users allows designers to identify any potential issues, as well as make sure that the kiosk is as user-friendly as possible.

Designing kiosks with accessibility in mind is a critical step in creating an equitable experience for all users. By understanding the differences between accessibility and usability, designing with an audience-focused approach, and testing with real users, designers can ensure their kiosks are as accessible and user-friendly as possible.

# 7. Finding a Balance Between Comfort and Convenience

The goal of every design is to create a product that is intuitive and easy to use. When it comes to kiosks, comfort and convenience must also be taken into consideration. In this chapter, we will explore the balance needed between comfort, convenience and usability. We will discuss how to design an ergonomic kiosk that meets user needs, from physical dimensions to environmental factors. Additionally, we will look at how to adjust elements, such as height and tilt, to ensure maximum comfort and convenience. Finally, we will discuss the importance of analyzing user feedback to guarantee an optimal user experience. Whether you are designing a kiosk for finance, healthcare or retail, this chapter will provide invaluable insights into creating a product that is both comfortable and convenient for users.

◤ Why Comfort and Convenience Matter: Uncovering the Benefits of Ergonomic Kiosk Design

It was a typical busy morning in the city. As the sun rose, people began to pour into the streets. Among the throngs of people was a woman in a wheelchair, determined to make it to work on time.

But that wasn't going to be so easy. She faced obstacles everywhere—sidewalks and intersections with no ramps, buildings with no accessible entrances, and too many steps. She was getting more frustrated with each passing minute; she couldn't even get into the train station.

Then by chance, she spotted the kiosk. Its adjustable height, tilt features, and handrails made it easy for her to use. She quickly realized that she could now purchase her train ticket and make it to her destination. She felt relieved and grateful for the accessibility the kiosk gave her.

This story illustrates how essential it is to design kiosks that meet the needs of users with disabilities. With the right balance of comfort and convenience, kiosks can make life easier and more enjoyable for people of all abilities.

◤ Understanding the Needs of Different Users

When designing a kiosk, it's important to take into account the needs of different user groups. This includes seniors, people with disabilities, and people with a variety of physical and mental abilities. By understanding the range of user activities and needs, you can ensure a kiosk that is comfortable and accessible to all.

When assessing the needs of different user groups, it's important to consider their physical requirements (such as reach and posture) as well as their mental requirements. For instance, a user with a visual impairment will require a different user experience than someone with normal vision. Similarly, a user with a physical disability will need access to adjustable features to make the kiosk comfortable for their own use.

The user environment is another key factor to consider when designing for user needs. Consider the type of environment in which the kiosk will be situated and how it might influence the user experience. Factors such as lighting, temperature, and noise can all affect the usability of the kiosk. As such, you should investigate these elements to ensure that the kiosk is accessible to all users.

When designing for different user needs, adjustable features can be an important consideration. Adjustable features such as height, tilt, and color can help customize the kiosk to the individual user. This can make the kiosk a more pleasant and efficient experience for all users, regardless of their abilities. Adjustable features may also help you meet other design objectives, such as increasing accessibility or creating a user-friendly interface.

Incorporating adjustable features also necessitates understanding the range of heights and angles that are comfortable for the user. For example, a taller kiosk may be more comfortable for a user with a physical disability. Similarly, a kiosk that is adjustable in both height and tilt can help a user with limited dexterity or mobility.

In order to ensure a kiosk design that is comfortable and convenient for all users, it is important to consider the balance between usability and convenience. The user journey should be analyzed to identify areas where convenience can be improved. Additionally, elements such as adjustable height, tilt features, and soundproofing can help ensure a comfortable user experience.

Finally, user feedback should be closely monitored and analyzed to ensure that the kiosk meets all comfort and convenience requirements. Testing, surveys, and customer sentiment can all provide valuable insights into the user experience and help to identify areas for improvement. By listening to users, you can make sure that your kiosk is comfortable and convenient to use for everyone.

❑ Understanding Physical Dimensions and Reach

When designing a kiosk with ergonomics in mind, it is important to take into account physical dimensions and reach. This involves analyzing user posture and understanding the physical reach requirements for each user. By planning the layout of the kiosk to maximize accessibility and carefully calculating the size, you can ensure that the kiosk is comfortable to use.

❑ Analyzing User Posture

The first step in understanding physical dimensions and reach is to analyze user posture while interacting with the kiosk. This involves observing the user in their natural environment and noting the way they interact with the kiosk. This will give you valuable insight into the posture and behavior that the kiosk should enable.

❑ Understanding Reach Requirements

Once you have observed the user's posture and behavior, you need to consider their reach requirements. This means understanding the physical space between the user and the kiosk, as well as the size of the user's hands. This will help you determine the size of the kiosk, as well as the positioning of key components.

❑ Planning the Layout

Once the physical reach requirements are established, the next step is to plan the layout of the kiosk. This is important for maximizing accessibility for different users. If the kiosk is not laid out properly, there could be a risk of users not being able to reach components that are important for their interaction. When planning the layout, consider the space available, the size of the user, and any physical accessibility requirements that may need to be met.

❑ Calculating Size

Once the layout and reach requirements have been established, it is necessary to calculate the size of the kiosk. This helps ensure that the kiosk is comfortable to use. Consider the size of the user's body and hands, their posture, and the reach requirements. Calculate the size based on these factors, and then adjust as necessary to ensure comfort.

By understanding the physical dimensions and reach of the user, and carefully considering the layout and size of the kiosk, you can ensure that your design is ergonomic and comfortable to use. Analyzing user posture and identifying reach requirements are important steps in designing an ergonomic kiosk that is accessible to all users. Once these requirements have been established, it is important to ensure that the kiosk is properly laid out and sized, to maximize accessibility and user comfort.

Creating accessible kiosks is about finding a balance between functionality and convenience. When designing kiosks, it is important to identify the primary user needs, such as speed, convenience, and accuracy. Understanding the key objectives and examining the user journey is essential for creating a kiosk that maximises convenience.

It is important to ensure the design addresses common user problems and simplifies the user experience. This may include incorporating adjustable features such as height and tilt, which can provide a more comfortable experience for different users. It is also vital to consider environmental factors such as lighting, temperature, and noise when creating a kiosk.

Lastly, user feedback is vital in ensuring that the kiosk meets all comfort and convenience needs. Obtaining feedback via surveys or testing can provide vital insights into the user experience. This feedback can then be used to implement changes that improve the usability of the kiosk. Analyzing the impact of these changes will then help to make sure that the design is successful in finding the right balance.

❏ Adjustable Height and Tilt Features

When designing a kiosk, it's important to consider the needs and comfort level of different users. Incorporating adjustable features into the design can make the kiosk easier and more comfortable for people with physical limitations, such as seniors and people with disabilities. Adjustable height and tilt features provide users with the ability to customize their experience and ensure that the kiosk suits their individual needs.

When researching the impact of adjustable features, it is important to consider the range of heights and angles that are comfortable for the user. The most comfortable angle for the user may depend on the user's physical reach, posture, and strength/range of motion. The size and weight of the kiosk also affects the user's experience; if the kiosk is too tall or too heavy, it may be uncomfortable or difficult to use.

It is also important to incorporate adjustable features with minimal disruption to the user experience. In other words, the user shouldn't have to expend too much time or effort to adjust the kiosk. Lever mechanisms and other methods of adjusting the height and tilt can be incorporated into the design, which makes it easy for the user to make changes.

In addition to adjustable height and tilt, there are a number of other features that can make a kiosk more comfortable and convenient for users. Soundproofing solutions can reduce the noise of the environment, while adjustable lighting and temperature controls can improve the user experience. Incorporating user feedback into the design, such as testing and surveys, can help identify the most comfortable usability features.

Finally, it is important to consider the balance of functionality and convenience when designing a kiosk. The physical dimensions and reach requirements of the user should always be taken into account. A kiosk that is too tall or too heavy can cause discomfort and inconvenience, while a kiosk that is too small may not be able to accommodate all the user's needs. The layout of the kiosk should be designed to maximize accessibility and convenience, while the adjustable features should be incorporated with minimal impact on the user experience. By making sure to consider the needs of different users, it is possible to create a kiosk that makes life easier for everyone.

❑ Environmental Factors in Kiosk Design

When designing an accessible kiosk, one must take into account a variety of environmental factors to ensure user comfort and convenience. These factors include lighting, temperature, and noise.

Lighting: Good lighting is essential for an accessible kiosk. Poor or inadequate lighting can be a barrier to people with disabilities, as it can prevent them from completing their tasks effectively, or even correctly. When designing an accessible kiosk, it is important to include lighting that is bright enough for all users to   complete

their tasks. Consider adding multiple light sources as well as an adjustable brightness setting. Additionally, adding a text-to-speech feature to kiosks can help reduce eye strain for users.

Temperature: Temperature can also be a major factor for kiosk usability. Too hot and users may find it uncomfortable to use the kiosk, and too cold and they may be unable to use it at all. When designing an accessible kiosk, consider the temperature of the environment where it will be placed. Taking into account the climate and the target user group, you can adjust the temperature of the kiosk accordingly to ensure user comfort.

Noise: The level of ambient noise can also be a factor in how accessible a kiosk is. Too much noise can be a barrier to people with hearing impairments or sensitivity to loud sounds. When designing an accessible kiosk, consider the noise level in the environment and look for ways to reduce it. Adding soundproofing or noise-cancelling features can be useful in this regard. Additionally, avoid adding audio that is too loud or jarring, as this can make it difficult to use the kiosk.

Ultimately, environmental factors such as lighting, temperature, and noise should all be taken into consideration when designing an accessible kiosk. Ensuring user comfort and convenience should be a priority, as this will ensure that the users can use the kiosk effectively and efficiently. By considering these factors, you can ensure that your kiosk design is as accessible and user-friendly as possible.

❑ Analyzing User Feedback

User feedback is an important tool when it comes to designing a kiosk that works well for all users. Gathering feedback from users can help you to identify issues and refine your design to meet everyone's needs. In this section, we will discuss how to analyze user feedback to ensure the kiosk meets all comfort and convenience requirements.

❑ Examining User Data

One way to examine user feedback is to analyze user data. By looking at how users interact with the kiosk, you can uncover trends in usability. By tracking user behavior, you can identify user patterns, such as which screens they are accessing and how they are navigating around the kiosk. You can then use this data to make changes to improve user experience.

❑ Gathering User Feedback

In addition to examining user data, it is important to gather user feedback directly from users. User testing is a great way to get feedback on how well the kiosk works. You can ask users to complete specific tasks to assess the ease of use and accessibility of the kiosk. You can also conduct surveys or interviews to find out what users think of the kiosk and what improvements they suggest.

❑ Understanding Customer Sentiment

Once you have gathered user feedback, it's important to understand the customer sentiment around the kiosk. User feedback can provide a lot of insight into how people feel towards the kiosk and how they are using it. This can be invaluable information when it comes to making the kiosk more accessible and user-friendly.

❑ Implementing Changes

Once you have identified areas of improvement based on user feedback, it's important to make changes to the kiosk to address those issues. This could be anything from changing the color scheme to adding new features. If you make changes to the kiosk, make sure to test it with users to ensure it meets their needs and is more user-friendly.

❑ Analyzing the Impact of Changes

Once you have made changes to the kiosk based on user feedback, it's important to analyze the impact of those changes. This will help you understand how effective the changes were and identify any further improvements that need to be made. This can also help you identify trends in customer satisfaction that can help inform future design decisions.

By taking into account user feedback and analyzing it to ensure the kiosk meets all comfort and convenience requirements, you can create a kiosk that's user friendly and accessible for everyone. Gathering and analyzing user feedback is an important part of the design process, so make sure you factor it into your design process when creating a kiosk.

❑ Finding a Balance

This chapter explored how to create a comfortable and convenient environment for users of a kiosk. It covered understanding the needs of different users, developing an ergonomic design, considering the balance between functionality and convenience, incorporating adjustable features, taking into account environmental factors and analyzing user feedback. Following these steps ensures that the kiosk is designed to meet the comfort and convenience needs of the users.

## ◥ Examples of Ergonomic Kiosk Design in Action

Person One:

Person one saw the importance of understanding the needs of their users. They took the time to do research and analyze feedback so they could design a kiosk that was suitable for everyone. They used adjustable height and tilt features to ensure that users of different physical dimensions had easy access to the kiosk. They also took into consideration environmental factors like lighting, temperature, and noise level when they designed it.

Person Two:

Person two was focused on creating an ergonomic design that was comfortable for all of their users. They designed a kiosk that allowed users to adjust the height, slope, and angle of the screen so that it would be easier to use for people with physical limitations. They also worked to make the kiosk as user friendly as possible with easy-to-understand navigation and instructions.

Person Three:

Person three aimed to create a kiosk that was both comfortable and convenient. They developed a design that incorporated adjustable height and tilt features, as well as adjustable monitor brightness, colors, and contrast. They also worked to make the interface as intuitive as possible, with simple menu and navigation options. To ensure users were comfortable, they also incorporated features such as automated lighting, temperature control, and sound dampening.

❏ A Step-by-Step Guide to Achieving Ergonomic Kiosk Design

Stage 1: Understanding the needs of different users in order to create a comfortable environment
- Research the needs of different types of users (disabilities, physical limitations, etc.)
- Identify any features that would be helpful in creating an accessible kiosk
- Consider the different ways people use kiosks (navigating with a cane, wheelchair, etc.)

Stage 2: Developing an ergonomic design that takes into account physical dimensions and reach
- Measure the average height, arm length, and reach of the kiosk user
- Design the kiosk to allow for comfortable usage
- Consider the range of motion the user would need in order to navigate the kiosk

Stage 3: Considering the balance of functionality and convenience when designing the kiosk
- Make sure the functionality of the kiosk is not sacrificed in order to make it more convenient
- Ensure that users can access the kiosk quickly and easily
- Test the usability of the kiosk from various angles

Stage 4: Incorporating elements such as adjustable height and tilt features
- Research adjustable features for kiosk design
- Design and implement an adjustable feature based on user needs
- Test to ensure the adjustable feature works properly

Stage 5: Taking into account environmental factors when designing the kiosk
- Analyze the environment where the kiosk is located
- Identify any potential environmental issues that could affect the kiosk (weather, dust, etc.)
- Design the kiosk to withstand environmental conditions

Stage 6: Analyzing user feedback to ensure the kiosk meets all comfort and convenience requirements
- Collect user feedback on the design of the kiosk
- Analyze the feedback to identify any areas of improvement
- Make any necessary changes to the design of the kiosk based on user feedback

## ◥ Applying a Useful Framework to Achieve Ergonomic Kiosk Design

❑ The "Reach, Adjust, Analyze" Framework

This approach encourages designers to:

Reach – Determine the physical dimensions and reach of users when designing the kiosk

Adjust – Incorporate adjustable height and tilt features, as well as environmental factors, into the design

Analyze – Analyze user feedback to ensure the kiosk meets all comfort and convenience requirements

## ◥ Common Mistakes to Avoid: Balancing Comfort and Convenience

One of the most common mistakes people make when designing a kiosk for accessibility is not considering the user interface. It's important to remember that everyone has different needs, and a user interface that works for some people may not work for all. For example, a user who is visually impaired may have difficulty reading large amounts of text, or a user with a physical disability may need larger buttons and font sizes. It's essential to take into account the needs of all users when designing the kiosk, and to ensure the interface is accessible to all.

Another mistake people make is not taking into account the environmental factors when designing the kiosk. Ambient lighting, temperature, humidity, and even sound can all affect the user experience. If the environment is too bright or loud, it can be uncomfortable and distracting. Also, if the kiosk is located in an area with poor air circulation, users may become overheated. Taking into account the environment when designing the kiosk can help ensure a more comfortable user experience.

Another common mistake made is not properly incorporating adjustable features. Many users need to adjust the kiosk to their own physical needs, such as adjusting the height or tilt features. If there are no adjustable features, it can be very difficult for the user to use the kiosk. It is important to remember that everyone has different needs, and not all users will find the same settings comfortable.

Finally, it is important to analyze user feedback after the kiosk has been installed. This can help ensure that the kiosk meets all comfort and convenience requirements. If the kiosk is not meeting the needs of its users, it can be difficult to make necessary changes without feedback. It is important to actively seek feedback from users and to evaluate the kiosk to ensure it meets all user needs.

In conclusion, there are several mistakes that people often make when designing kiosks for accessibility. It is important to consider the user interface, environmental factors, adjustable features and user feedback when designing the kiosk. By incorporating these considerations into the design of the kiosk, it can be ensured that the kiosk is accessible and comfortable for all users.

## 8. How to Test Kiosks for Accessibility

This chapter is all about how to test kiosks for accessibility. We will explore different methods of testing and how to identify user needs and preferences in order to create an effective and efficient testing plan. You'll learn the ins and outs of manual testing, various automated tools and how to evaluate the usability and user experience. You'll also be able to create an accessibility testing plan that complies with the existing standards and ensures that your kiosks are accessible for everyone. So let's get started on your journey to making sure your kiosks are as accessible as possible.

◥ Why Accessibility Testing Is Critical: A Guide to Making Your Kiosks Accessible for Everyone

Mandy was at the mall, wheeling her chair through the busy crowds, when she spotted it—the newest kiosk. Excited, she wheeled closer, anxious to use the kiosk and get the item she needed. But her excitement turned to disappointment when she realized the kiosk was too high for her to reach and there were no accessible features. She felt embarrassed and defeated.

Luckily, Mandy was not alone. A store employee noticed her struggle and made a quick phone call to the kiosk designer. After some discussion, the designer realized that if the kiosk had been designed with accessibility in mind, it would have been usable for Mandy. So, the designer redesigned the kiosk, adding features that would enable customers with disabilities to use the kiosk with ease.

Mandy was overjoyed when she returned to the mall and saw the new accessible kiosk. She was able to wheel up to the kiosk, use it without any issues, and get the item she needed. She felt empowered, knowing that her voice had been heard and that her needs had been taken into account. Designing kiosks with accessibility in mind truly makes a difference!

❑ How to Test Kiosks for Accessibility

Testing your kiosk designs for accessibility is important to ensure that they are usable by everyone, no matter their abilities or disabilities. By designing with accessibility in mind and testing your kiosks, you can make sure that everyone can easily access and use your kiosks.

The first step in testing your kiosks for accessibility is to understand the scope of the testing. The most commonly used accessibility standards to adhere to are the Web Content Accessibility Guidelines (WCAG) and the Americans with Disabilities Act (ADA). These guidelines and standards provide a set of criteria for your kiosks to meet and are essential to ensure that your kiosks are accessible to all. When creating an accessibility testing plan, it's important to consider the areas that need to be tested within the scope of these guidelines. This may include testing for keyboard accessibility, image alt text, mouse navigation, visual design, audio content, and more.

Additionally, it's important to identify user needs and preferences. You can do this by conducting user research. This may include surveys or interviews with users or potential users to understand how people interact with your kiosk designs and what needs or preferences they may have. Analyzing user feedback from reviews, comments, and other sources is also a great way to understand user preferences. Additionally, evaluating usability issues such as clarity of design, ease of use, intuitiveness, and consistency can all help you identify areas for improvement in your design.

The next step is to perform manual testing on the kiosk. This may include using a variety of testing approaches such as keyboard navigation and mouse navigation to check the functionality of the kiosk. Additionally, you may want to test the visual design of the kiosk to check for clarity and contrast. You can also check for accessibility issues that may arise with audio, video, and other content.

After the manual tests have been completed, you can evaluate the usability and user experience of the kiosk design. Usability principles can be used to measure effectiveness of the user experience, such as efficiency, satisfaction, intuitiveness, and consistency. Additionally, you should check for errors, user feedback, and other issues that may be present in the design. Identifying areas for improvement in the design, such as navigation, performance, and other features, can help you create a better kiosk experience.

In addition to manual testing, you should also consider automated testing for compliance with the accessibility standards. Automated testing can make the process much faster and more efficient, ensuring consistency and accuracy. Automated tools such as WAVE or ARIA can be used to review your kiosk designs for accessibility issues. Additionally, techniques such as accessibility checks and code validation can be used to make sure your design meets the standards.

Finally, create an accessibility testing plan that meets all the standards. Developing an accessibility testing plan is important to ensure that all the tests are completed correctly and all areas of the kiosk are checked. This will include creating objectives, identifying testing methods, and creating checklists and timelines to make sure everything is accounted for. Additionally, you'll need to document the results of the tests and create a plan to resolve any accessibility issues.

Overall, understanding the scope of accessibility testing, identifying user needs and preferences, performing manual testing on the kiosk, and using automated tools to test for compliance are all important steps when testing your kiosks for accessibility. Creating a comprehensive accessibility testing plan will ensure that your design meets the standards and is usable by all.

❑ Identifying User Needs and Preferences

User needs and preferences are key elements that should be taken into consideration when designing a kiosk to be accessible for all. It is important to understand the specific needs and preferences of your users in order to create an optimal user experience. This can be done through user research and surveys, and by collecting user feedback.

User research and surveys can help you to understand what users need and expect from your kiosks. Surveys can provide a deeper level of understanding by giving users the chance to voice their opinions and share what is important to them. It is important to keep user research and surveys up to date as user needs and preferences can change over time.

User feedback is important when designing an accessible kiosk as it gives us the opportunity to directly hear from users. There are various methods of collecting user feedback, such as reviews, comments, surveys, etc. By actively seeking feedback from users, we can identify usability issues and user preferences that should be incorporated into the design.

When evaluating usability issues, it is important to consider the clarity of the kiosk design, as well as the ease of use. People with disabilities may require an extra level of clarity when using the kiosk, and ensuring that users understand the interface and can easily navigate it is key. Additionally, designing an intuitive user experience is important and can be achieved through testing with real users and closely analysing user feedback.

Once you have identified the needs and preferences of users, you can start to identify areas for improvement. This could include features that can be implemented, such as voice control or alternative input methods, or updates to the visual design. It is important to consider the impact that any changes or additions will have on the accessibility of the kiosk.

By understanding user needs and preferences, analysing user feedback and evaluating usability issues, you can ensure that your kiosk design is accessible and that it meets the needs of users with disabilities. With careful consideration and continual testing, your kiosk design can be improved to benefit all users.

❑ Performing Manual Testing on the Kiosk

Manual testing is an essential part of designing an accessible kiosk. Manual testing will allow you to identify accessibility issues that may not be detectable by automated tools. It can also be used to evaluate a kiosk's user experience and usability.

When manually testing a kiosk, you should create a checklist of areas that need to be tested. This should include keyboard access, image alt text, and other accessibility features. You should also consider manual testing guidelines such as keyboard navigation, mouse navigation, and other input methods. This will help ensure that your kiosk is accessible to a wide range of users.

In addition to testing for the accessibility of your kiosk, you should also pay attention to visual design issues. Visual design relies heavily on clarity and contrast. If these elements are not well-defined, users may have trouble understanding the information being presented. It is important to ensure that any images or videos used are well-defined and readable to people with disabilities.

Finally, you should also test for accessibility issues with audio, video, and other multimedia content. This can include checking for captioning accuracy, verifying audio input and output, and ensuring that the video or audio content is accessible to people with vision or hearing impairments.

By performing manual testing on your kiosk, you can ensure that the kiosk is accessible to everyone. It is important to take the time to check all aspects of your kiosk to ensure that it is user-friendly and accessible to people with disabilities. Manual testing will help you create a more inclusive user experience and result in an accessible kiosk.

❑ Evaluating Usability and User Experience

Getting your kiosk to a place where it meets the standards for accessibility is one thing; getting it to a place where it is easy and enjoyable to use is quite another. It is vital that you take the time to evaluate the usability and user experience of your kiosk to make sure that it is not only accessible, but that it is also comfortable and easy to use.

Usability principles are the key to creating an enjoyable user experience. The main principle is intuitiveness—making sure that it is natural and intuitive for the user to complete tasks. Consistency is also critical; users should not have to relearn how to use your kiosk every time they come across it.

To make sure you are providing a good user experience, it is essential that you set out a checklist of issues to be checked. When you are thinking about usability, you should consider factors such as errors, user feedback, and ease of use. It is also important to measure the effectiveness of the user experience by looking at factors such as efficiency and user satisfaction. This will help you to identify areas of your kiosk that require improvement.

In terms of navigation, users should be able to navigate your kiosk with ease. This means that navigation should be logical, efficient, and make it easy to complete tasks. Additionally, you should evaluate how well your kiosk performs, especially when it comes to response times and speeds of loading. Making sure that your kiosk is fast and reliable will help with user satisfaction.

Finally, you should be aware of some key accessibility issues which may impact the user experience. Make sure that text size can be adjusted, that images have alternative text describing them, and that there is an adequate colour contrast between text and the background. With these guidelines in mind, you can ensure that the usability and user experience of your kiosk is the very best it can be.

❏ Testing for Accessibility Compliance with Automated Tools

When it comes to ensuring accessibility compliance, automated tools are the way to go. Automated tools are computer programs that scan websites and other digital content to identify potential issues with accessibility. They provide a fast, accurate, and consistent way of ensuring that your kiosks are accessible to all users.

These tools take the guesswork out of testing for accessibility compliance. With automated tools, there is no need to manually test each of the features of your kiosk. Automated tools are designed to provide an in-depth analysis of the accessibility of the kiosks, so you can be confident that they are up to code.

There are a few types of automated tools available. The most popular ones are scanning tools which go through the code of a website and detect any potential issues with it. These tools are great for finding issues like missing alt tags, improperly labeled form inputs, and other potential issues.

Another type of automated tool is a screen reader. Screen readers are designed to be used by people with vision impairments, and they read the content of a website out loud. By using a screen reader, you can test how well the content is being read and understand any potential issues that may not be visible to the naked eye.

Finally, there are a few different testing tools available. The most popular are WAVE, which checks for issues with accessibility, and ARIA, which is an accessibility taxonomy for web applications. With these tools, you can easily detect any issues with accessibility on your kiosks.

Once you have chosen the automated tools to use, it is important to create an accessibility testing plan. This will help you ensure that you are testing all areas of accessibility, and that you are doing so in a consistent and thorough manner. The plan should include a checklist of items to be tested, as well as any timelines or budgets that need to be adhered to.

Testing for accessibility compliance with automated tools is an effective way to ensure that your kiosks are accessible to all users. Not only does it take the guesswork out of testing, but it is also much faster and more comprehensive than manual testing. By using these tools, you can be sure that your kiosks are up to code with the latest accessibility standards.

❏ Creating an Accessibility Testing Plan

Creating an accessibility testing plan is essential when designing kiosks to make them accessible to people with disabilities. Before you begin the testing process, you must develop a plan that outlines the objectives, testing methodology, and steps to take in order to ensure accessibility.

❑ Objectives

The first step in creating an accessibility testing plan is to develop objectives for the testing process. These objectives should be specific and measurable, and should reflect the goals of the project. Ask yourself questions like: What accessibility requirements need to be met? What is the timeline for testing, and what are the milestones to be achieved? Answering these questions will help you to determine the objectives of your testing plan.

❑ Testing Methodology

Once you've determined the objectives, you need to decide on the testing methodology. You can choose from manual testing, automated tools, or a combination of the two. Manual testing involves manually checking the kiosk and testing each feature to see if it meets the criteria of the applicable accessibility standards. Automated tools provide a more detailed analysis and can give a much more accurate overall assessment of the kiosk's accessibility.

❑ Documentation and Reporting

Creating and documenting a checklist of areas to be tested is another important step in the process. This checklist should include testing all components of the kiosk, as well as tests for individual features. Once testing is complete, the results should be recorded and a report should be created. This report should include any issues that were identified, as well as a timeline with milestones for resolving any issues.

❑ Steps for Resolving Accessibility Issues

Finally, when any issues are identified, the next step is to put a plan in place to resolve them. This plan should include testing the kiosk again to ensure that all accessibility requirements have been met. The timeline for this should be outlined and milestones should be established based on the objectives that were set out at the beginning of the process.

Creating a comprehensive and up-to-date accessibility testing plan is essential when designing kiosks to make them accessible to people with disabilities. Developing objectives, testing methodology, and steps for resolving any issues will ensure that the kiosk meets all the necessary requirements. By following these steps, you can confidently create kiosks that are accessible to all.

❏ Conclusion

In this chapter, we discussed how to properly test kiosks for accessibility. We looked at the scope of accessibility testing and how to use both manual and automated tests to assess usability and user experience. Additionally, we discussed how to create an accessibility testing plan that meets standards. By following these steps, you can ensure that your kiosks are accessible and compliant with the necessary regulations.

◥ Seeing Accessibility in Action: Examples of Implementing Accessible Kiosks

1. Bill was responsible for testing the kiosks at his city hall. He wanted to make sure they were accessible to all users, so he used a combination of manual and automated testing. He consulted with users with disabilities to identify their needs and preferences. Then he tested the kiosks himself, using a range of standards and criteria to ensure they met accessibility requirements. Finally, he developed an accessibility testing plan that included regular reviews to ensure the kiosks remained accessible.

2. Jenny launched an online store and was concerned about making sure the website was accessible to everyone. She researched accessibility standards and requirements, and then identified the automated tools she could use to test for compliance. She manually tested the website and identified areas for improvement, then used the automated tools to look for any issues that could cause a problem for people with disabilities. After she made the necessary changes, she set up a schedule for regular testing and review to ensure the website remained accessible.

3. John was working on a new mobile app for his company. He wanted to make sure the app was accessible to everyone who might need to use it. He created a testing plan, which included both manual and automated tests. He consulted with users with disabilities to understand their needs and preferences. Then he performed manual tests, using a variety of criteria to test for accessibility

compliance. He also used automated tools to make sure the app met the required standards. Finally, he implemented a regular testing and review schedule to ensure that the app was accessible.

## ◤ Step-By-Step Guide to Testing Kiosks for Accessibility

Understand the scope of your accessibility testing:
- Research and become familiar with the most common accessibility requirements
- Determine the scope of testing that needs to be done (i.e., are other media types such as audio, video, documents, etc. involved?)
- Set up a testing environment with the necessary tools and systems

Identify user needs and preferences:
- Research and gain an understanding of the needs of people with disabilities
- Speak with people with disabilities regarding their preferences for using kiosks
- Survey other users to determine their preferences

Perform manual testing on the kiosk:
- Check keyboard input, mouse input and key mappings
- Test color contrast and text size
- Evaluate the navigation and tab order of different pages

Evaluate the usability and user experience:
- Ask people with disabilities to test the kiosk
- Gather feedback from the testers
- Make any necessary changes

Use automated tools to test for accessibility compliance:
- Research and select the appropriate automated tool for testing
- Utilize the automated tool to test the kiosk for compliance with accessibility standards
- Review the automated tool's report and make any necessary changes

Create an accessibility testing plan that meets standards:

- Create a testing plan that outlines the steps involved in the process

- Ensure that the plan meets all relevant accessibility standards

- Document the results of each phase of the testing process.

## ◼ Using a Step-by-Step Framework to Test Kiosks for Accessibility

The PASS Framework:

P - Prioritize user needs and preferences

A - Automate accessibility testing

S - Simulate manual testing

S - Ensure compliance with standards

## ◼ Common Mistakes to Avoid When Testing Kiosks for Accessibility

Many people mistakenly think that accessibility only means making a website or application work with a screen reader. While providing compatibility with a screen reader is an important part of accessibility, that isn't all there is to it. People often overlook the fact that accessibility involves more than just making a website or application visible to those with disabilities; it's also about making the experience just as accessible and user-friendly for those with disabilities as it is for everyone else.

For example, when designing a kiosk, people often overlook the importance of good color contrast for people with vision impairments. For example, if white text is placed on a light gray background, it may be difficult for someone with a vision impairment to read the text. Ideally, you should strive for a minimum contrast ratio of 4.5:1 between the text and the background color to ensure that the text is easy to read.

Usability is another key element of kiosk accessibility that is often overlooked. Many people assume that just because a kiosk has been designed for people with disabilities, it will be easy to use for those same people. Unfortunately, this is not always the case. People with disabilities may not be familiar with the same technology used by a kiosk as those without disabilities, and may need more cues or guidance to help them perform a task. It's important to provide user-friendly interfaces that are well-labeled, intuitive, and easy to navigate.

People also often underestimate the amount of time and effort required to test a kiosk for accessibility. It's not enough to just make sure it works with a screen reader - you need to thoroughly test how people with disabilities interact with the device. This may involve testing the kiosk in person, as well as using automated tools to scan for any potential accessibility issues. For example, automated tools can detect if a kiosk has color contrast issues or if there are any usability problems that could make it difficult for someone with disabilities to use.

It's important to remember that accessibility isn't just about making sure a website or application is visible to those with disabilities; it's also about making sure the experience is just as accessible and user-friendly for those with disabilities as it is for everyone else. By understanding the principles of universal design, creating user-friendly interfaces, and performing thorough accessibility testing, you can ensure that the kiosk you design is accessible to people with disabilities.

## 9. The Challenges of Alternative Inputs

Alternative input methods are becoming increasingly more important in kiosk design as users' needs become more diverse in terms of accessibility. In this chapter, we discuss the various challenges associated with implementing alternative input techniques into your kiosk design. We'll explain the importance of considering the needs of users when choosing the type of input and how to implement alternate input capabilities in a kiosk. You'll learn how to ensure compatibility for any input method you decide to use and how to test usability with various alternative inputs. We'll also explore ways to stay up to date with advancements in alternative input methods. By the end of the chapter, you'll have a deeper understanding of the challenges and best practices associated with alternative input methods.

◗ Unlock Accessibility with Alternative Inputs and Enhance Your Kiosk Design

A warm summer day on the beach. Joe, who has cerebral palsy, is with his family and they are excited to use the new interactive kiosk at the nearby beach house. Joe struggles to move his hands due to his disability and is worried that he won't be able to use the kiosk. But his family is determined to help him and they search out an alternative input method that can work for him. After some trial and error, they find a system that supports a mouthstick, which Joe can use to access the kiosk. With the help of the new input method, Joe is able to successfully navigate the kiosk and enjoy the day at the beach with his family. This experience demonstrates the importance of having alternative input methods available to ensure that people with disabilities are able to fully utilize interactive kiosks.

❑ Understanding Alternative Input Methods

When it comes to designing kiosks for accessibility, alternative input methods can be just as important as visual and audio outputs. Alternative input methods include any form of input other than a traditional physical keyboard and mouse. These methods are often used by people with disabilities as an alternative way to interact with a kiosk.

Alternative input methods include voice recognition, eye-tracking, touchscreens, switches, and other specialized interfaces. Each of these methods has its own set of pros and cons. It's important to understand these differences in order to select the best option for each kiosk.

❑ Voice Recognition

Voice recognition is a form of input that allows users to control the kiosk using their voice. Voice recognition can be used in a variety of ways, such as issuing commands, entering text, and even navigations menus. It can also recognize multiple languages.

The main benefit of voice recognition is that it requires very little physical interaction with the kiosk. It's a great option for users who are unable to use a physical keyboard or mouse. The downside, however, is that it is less accurate than other input methods and can be easily confused by background noise.

❑ Eye-Tracking

Eye-tracking is a form of input that uses the user's eye movements to control the kiosk. Eye-tracking uses sophisticated cameras, algorithms, and software to track the user's eyes and interpret them as commands. The input can be used for tasks such as navigating menus, selecting items, and entering commands.

The main benefit of eye-tracking is that it allows users with limited mobility to access a kiosk with very little physical interaction. It is also more accurate than voice recognition, as it is not easily confused by background noise. The downside, however, is that it requires the user to have good vision and pay close attention to the kiosk in order to use it effectively.

❑ Touchscreens

Touchscreens are a form of input that allows users to interact with the kiosk using touch or gestures. Touchscreens offer a variety of input options, such as tapping and swiping. They are often used to navigate menus, select items, and enter commands.

The main benefit of touchscreens is that they are easy to use and require very little physical interaction. They are also very intuitive, making them a great option for inexperienced users. The downside, however, is that they require the user to have good vision and dexterity.

❑ Switches

Switches are a form of tactile input that allow the user to interact with the kiosk using physical buttons or switches. These buttons or switches can be used to enter commands, select options, and navigate menus.

The main benefit of switches is that they allow users with limited mobility or dexterity to interact with the kiosk. They also require very little physical interaction and are easy to use. The downside, however, is that they require users to have good vision in order to read the labels on the buttons or switches.

❑ Conclusion

Alternative input methods are a great way to make kiosks accessible for people with disabilities. Each of the methods discussed here has its own set of pros and cons. It's important to understand these differences in order to select the best option for each kiosk. With the right input method, you can ensure that all users will be able to access and use the kiosk with ease.

❑ Considering the Needs of Users When Choosing the Type of Input

When you're designing a kiosk, one of the most important considerations is choosing the right type of input. Every user is going to have different needs, so it's important to take these into account when selecting an input type.

First of all, it's important to identify the user's needs. This will help inform what type of input will work best for that person. For example, if the user has limited dexterity, an on-screen keyboard may be a better choice than using a physical one. Similarly, if the user has a visual impairment, voice recognition may be the best choice.

Next, it's important to contextualize the input types. This means understanding how the various types of input will be used in the kiosk environment. For example, some methods of input may not be suitable for low-light environments, while others may have compatibility issues with certain devices.

Finally, it's important to consider the user's preferences when selecting the input type. Some users may prefer to use a traditional keyboard, while others may find voice recognition or a touch screen more comfortable. Ultimately, it's important to give the user the best possible experience, so take the time to choose an input type that they find most comfortable.

By taking the time to identify user needs, contextualize input types and consider user preferences, you can ensure that the kiosk you design is truly accessible to all.

❏ Implementing Alternate Input Capabilities in a Kiosk

When designing and building a kiosk, it's important to consider the needs of all users.

This means ensuring that the kiosk supports various input methods so that anyone can access the kiosk, whether they are able-bodied, disabled or otherwise. Here, we will look at the different types of alternative input methods that can be integrated into a kiosk and the considerations for implementing them.

❏ Hardware Requirements for Each Type of Input

The primary hardware requirement for a kiosk to accept various inputs is a USB port. This will allow users to connect peripheral devices such as keyboards, mice, joystick, and other input devices. Additionally, a kiosk should be able to interpret standard commands from any type of input device. This includes touchscreens, speech recognition, video cameras, and any other form of user input.

❏ Integrating Input Type Into Existing Kiosk Design

When adding alternative input types to a kiosk, it is important to consider the user experience and ensure that the device is easy and intuitive to use. Additionally, the input type should be integrated in a way that makes the kiosk aesthetically pleasing and blends into the existing design. For example, if using a touch screen, consider whether it should be a small-format device or a larger one. Additionally, if integrating a joystick or other physical device, make sure to place it in an accessible and easy to reach area.

❏ Compatibility of User Interface and Any External Software

Another consideration when implementing alternative input methods is making sure that the user interface and any external software are compatible with the chosen input type. For example, if someone is using a joystick to make selections, the user interface should display clearly the options available and how to interact with the kiosk. Additionally, if any external software is being used, make sure to confirm that it too is compatible with the input method that the kiosk is using.

❑ Conclusion

When considering alternative input methods for a kiosk, it is important to keep in mind the hardware required, the integration into the existing kiosk design, and the compatibility of the user interface and any external software. Additionally, it is important to make sure that the chosen input type is easy and intuitive to use and provides a user experience that is visually pleasing. Taking all of these considerations into account will ensure that the kiosk is usable and accessible for anyone who needs to use it.

❑ Ensuring Compatibility Across Platforms

When it comes to making a kiosk accessible, compatibility across different platforms and devices is key. Whether the kiosk is a desktop computer, smartphone, tablet, or other device, it needs to be able to recognize and respond correctly to the user's input. To ensure compatibility, it's important to consider the systems and hardware that the kiosk will be running on and the type of input the user is likely to use.

❑ Testing for Accessibility

When designing a kiosk, it's vital to test for accessibility. This means ensuring that the kiosk can be used by all users, whether they have limited hearing, vision, mobility, physical dexterity, or cognitive abilities. It's important to test the kiosk with all of these abilities in mind, in order to ensure that it's properly accessible for all users.

❑ Developing Interfaces and Processes

When developing a kiosk, certain interfaces and processes may need to be built in order to support the different input types that the kiosk may need to respond to. Depending on the type of input, the interface and process needed may vary. For example, if the kiosk is designed to recognize voice input, special software and hardware may need to be integrated in order to process the input correctly.

In order to ensure compatibility across devices and platforms, interfaces and processes that support the input should be thoroughly tested and checked for accuracy. This will help ensure that the kiosk is as accessible as possible for all types of users.

## Testing for Usability with Alternative Inputs

In this subsection, we will look at testing for usability when using various alternative input methods. It is important to do this in order to ensure that the kiosk is accessible to as many people as possible, and that the kiosk interface is easy to use.

The first step is to test different input types to access the kiosk's content. This step involves ensuring that the kiosk is compatible with various input methods, such as voice recognition, alternate keyboards, and any other special input procedures. Additionally, make sure that the user interface is intuitive and user friendly. It should be easy for the user to figure out how to access the content they need, regardless of what input method they use.

The second step is to test the user's navigation of the kiosk's functionality. It is important that the interface is easy to use, and that all of the features can be accessed quickly and efficiently. Additionally, ensure that the user can easily switch between different input methods. If the user has to jump through hoops in order to access the content they need, they will likely be frustrated and turn away from the kiosk.

The third step is to develop metrics to measure the performance of different inputs. This can be done by creating surveys, testing the reaction of users, or running usability tests. Additionally, it may be useful to use analytics tools to track how users access the kiosk's content. This data can then be analyzed to determine how easy the kiosk's interface is to use, and how successful users are at navigating the kiosk.

In conclusion, testing for usability with various alternative inputs is an important step in creating accessible kiosks. By testing for compatibility with various input methods, testing navigation, and developing metrics to measure performance, you can ensure that your kiosk is accessible and easy to use for all users.

❏ Staying Up to Date with Advancements in Alternative Input Methods

Staying informed on the latest advancements in alternative input methods is essential for designing kiosks that are accessible to everyone. Fortunately, there are a number of emerging technologies, products, and services that can help you ensure that your kiosk is always up to date with the newest accessibility regulations.

❏ Voice Recognition

Voice recognition technology has seen tremendous advances in recent years. This technology can now recognize a broad range of accents and languages, and can allow people to interact with your kiosk without the need for physical input. This kind of technology can be extremely useful for people with physical disabilities.

It's important to remember that voice recognition technology is not always perfect. It's important to test how your kiosk responds to different accents, as well as how well it recognizes different words or phrases. Additionally, it's important to consider the interface design when using this kind of technology. Ensure that your kiosk is easy to understand, and that its responses are easy to interpret.

❏ New Products and Services

As accessibility advances, new products and services are being created to make life easier for people with disabilities. Staying informed about any new products or services that are available can help you stay up to date with the latest trends and technologies.

For example, the Apple Watch has recently become popular for people with disabilities. It's an easy way to make your kiosk accessible to those with physical impairments, by allowing them to access the kiosk using their watch instead of a mouse or keyboard.

❑ Special Keyboards and Adaptive Tools

Finally, it's important to explore software solutions that can help you make your kiosk accessible. Special keyboards and other adaptive tools can be extremely useful for people with physical or cognitive impairments. It's important to test any of these tools to ensure that they are comfortable to use, and that they will work with any other hardware or software you have installed on the kiosk.

By staying up to date with the latest advancements in alternate input methods, you can ensure that your kiosks remain accessible to everyone. Keep an eye out for new technologies, products and services, and explore special keyboards and other adaptive tools to make your kiosk as accessible as possible. With the right knowledge and resources, you can design kiosks that are accessible to everyone.

❑ Conclusion

This chapter discussed the various challenges associated with using alternative inputs in kiosks. A variety of input methods, such as voice recognition, eye-tracking and multi-touch, were discussed. It was emphasized that when choosing the type of input, it is essential to consider the needs of users. Furthermore, implementation of these input devices should be tested for compatibility and usability. Keeping up to date with advancements in alternative inputs is also important. Overall, this chapter has provided insights into the considerations that must be taken into account when selecting and utilizing alternative input methods for kiosks.

◤ Example Implementations to Unlock Accessibility and Enhance Kiosk Design

Person One:
Sarah had to design a kiosk for a library with patrons of all abilities. She researched the different types of alternative input methods, from speech recognition to joystick controls. She then considered the needs of her users and chose the most suitable input type to include in her kiosk, ensuring it was compatible with other devices. She tested the kiosk with different input methods, making sure that it was easy to use. Finally, she stayed up to date with the latest input methods so that her

kiosk was always accessible.

Person Two:

John needed to create a kiosk for a school, with students of all abilities. He looked into the different alternative input methods, such as eye tracking and adaptive keyboards. He carefully considered the needs of all his users, selecting the most suitable input type to include in his kiosk. He made sure that the input type he chose was compatible with other devices. He tested the kiosk with different alternative inputs, making sure it was easy to use. He kept up with the newest developments in alternative input methods so that his kiosk would always be accessible.

Person Three:

Linda had to design a kiosk for an office with employees of all abilities. She researched the different types of alternative input methods, such as touch screens and text-to-speech. She then thought carefully about the needs of her users and chose the best input type to include in her kiosk. She checked that the input type was compatible with other devices. She tested the kiosk with a variety of alternative inputs, making sure it was easy to use. Finally, she kept up with the latest alternative input methods so that her kiosk was always accessible.

## ◣ A Step-by-Step Guide to Enhancing Kiosk Design with Alternative Inputs

Understanding the Different Alternative Input Methods Available:

1. Read up on different input methods

2. Research which alternative input methods work best for different disabilities

3. Discuss different input methods with professionals in the field

Considering the Needs of Users When Choosing the Type of Input:

1. Identify the needs of the users who will interact with the kiosk

2. Establish which of the different input methods best suit the needs of the users

3. Make sure that all users will be able to operate the kiosk

Implementing Alternate Input Capabilities in a Kiosk:

1. Install the necessary hardware and software for the chosen input methods

2. Train staff to use the input method

3. Create instructions for users about how to operate the kiosk with the selected input method

Ensuring Compatibility for Any Input Method Used:

1. Research to make sure the input method will be compatible with the device

2. Test the input method on the device prior to implementation

Testing for Usability with Various Alternative Inputs:

1. Observe users interacting with the device to see if the input methods are comfortable and easy to use

2. Ask users for feedback about the input methods

3. Make changes as needed for improved usability

Staying Up to Date with Advancements in Alternative Input Methods:

1. Monitor industry news to read about advances in input methods

2. Attend industry events and conferences to learn more about current input trends

3. Compare the latest input methods with existing methods to see what improvements can be made

## ◗ Understand the Benefits of a Step-by-Step Guide for Enhancing Kiosk Design with Alternative Inputs

The DIAD Formula:

- Determine the disability/impairment.
- Identify the appropriate alternative input.
- Assess the compatibility with the kiosk.
- Design the kiosk experience.

## ◗ Common Mistakes to Avoid When Implementing Alternative Inputs

When designing a kiosk, many people assume that the user experience is the same for everyone, regardless of their ability. This couldn't be further from the truth. People with disabilities have unique needs that must be taken into account when designing a kiosk.

The first mistake people make is forgetting to consider alternative input methods. Kiosks are often designed with only a touch screen or on-screen keyboard in mind, without considering other input methods such as physical keyboards, eye control, and voice recognition. Without considering alternative input methods, kiosks may be unusable for people with certain disabilities.

Another mistake people make is failing to make software and hardware compatible with each other. Alternative inputs require software and hardware that are specifically designed to work together. Without the necessary compatibility, kiosks may not be able to detect the alternative input and therefore may be unusable.

People often fail to make the kiosk user-friendly enough. The kiosk needs to be designed in a way that gives users the comfort and confidence to quickly interact with it. Things such as easy-to-understand navigation paths, large, clear icons, and adjustable font sizes can help make the interface more user-friendly for everyone.

Kiosks also need to be tested for usability with different input methods. Even if the kiosk design is accessible, it will be unusable if the kiosk is not tested for compatibility with the input method. Testing ensures that the kiosk design works with the input methods selected, allowing users with disabilities to use the kiosk.

Lastly, it's important to stay aware of advances related to alternative input methods. Technology is constantly evolving, and it is important to stay up to date with new developments in alternative input methodologies. This allows designers to take advantage of new input methods, making kiosks even more accessible.

When it comes to designing kiosks, there are many small but important details that need to be taken into account. It is important to consider alternative input methods, ensure software and hardware compatibility, make the user interface user-friendly, test for usability, and stay up to date with advancements in alternative input methods. Doing so will ensure that everyone has access to an enjoyable and usable kiosk experience.

# 10. Designing for Ease of Use

In this chapter, we will explore how to design for ease of use, with a focus on understanding the importance of making sure a product is usable for all users. We will cover topics such as user-centered design, identifying user needs and ability levels, developing a consistent user interface, determining the best interaction methods, and analysing and improving the user experience. This chapter will provide valuable insight into how to create an enjoyable and accessible user experience that is tailored to the individual. If you're interested in creating products that are easy to use and accessible to all, this chapter is for you!

❑ Why it's Important to Design with Ease of Use in Mind

There was a wheelchair-bound man named Jacob who had taken a drive to the park near his home. He was a frequent visitor of the park and would often come with his family. This day, however, he had come alone. He wasn't exactly sure what he was looking for, but he was determined to find something to do.

As he rolled along the path, he noticed a vending machine that he had never seen before. It was a kiosk, and when he rolled up to it he could see that it was designed specifically for people with disabilities. He was excited to see that the buttons were large and clearly labeled and there was an accessible keypad that allowed him to input his selections.

Jacob punched in his selection and was absolutely stunned when the vending machine immediately responded and delivered his selection. He was so pleased to be able to do this task on his own and not have to ask for help! He thanked the kiosk designers for making such an empowering product and smiled as he rolled away, feeling independent and excited to explore the park further.

❑ Designing for Ease of Use

Usability has become increasingly important for product design in recent years. In order to create a successful design that's not just aesthetically pleasing but also easy for people to use, designers need to understand what User Experience (UX) and usability entails.

User Experience (UX) is the overall experience of the user when interacting with a product. It involves how easy it is to use the product, how efficient it is to use, how enjoyable it is to interact with, and its overall reliability. Usability on the other hand is focused on how easy it is for a user to interact with a product by understanding its core features and functions. It's also related to accessibility, which is the process of making sure that a product can be used by users regardless of their background, ability, or disability.

The importance of usability for product design is two-fold. First, if a product is difficult to use, its user engagement will be low and customers will stop using it. Second, when a product is easy to use, it can help increase customer satisfaction and loyalty. That's why designers need to fully understand their customer base and create a design that's tailored to their needs in order to create a successful product.

There are several strategies that can be used to improve a product's usability. Alpha/beta testing is when a product is tested by a select group of users before its public release, which can help identify any usability issues. User feedback is also invaluable, as customers can provide direct feedback on a product's usability. Lastly, there is also the option of conducting research by examining user data and analyzing user behavior.

By understanding the importance of usability for product design and how to improve it, designers can create successful products that are not only aesthetically pleasing but also easy to use. By focusing on their customer's needs, designers can create products that help customers be more productive and satisfied. When designers can create easy-to-use products, it helps create an overall positive customer experience and builds customer loyalty in the long run.

❑ Designing for User-Centricity

Creating effective products is all about understanding user needs and preferences. User-Centric design puts users at the center of the design process, to ensure the product or service meets their needs and wants. It considers access, usability, personalization, user feedback and other factors to ensure an optimal user experience.

❑ What is User-Centric Design?

User-Centric design is a design process that focuses on user goals, needs, values and preferences. It is an iterative design process that revises designs based on user feedback, which allows the product to be tailored to users. User-Centric design what results in a product or service that is tailored to the user, rather than a generic product that all users must conform to.

❑ Principles of User-Centric Design

User-Centric design has several core principles, including accessibility, personalization, user feedback and usability.

Accessibility refers to making sure the product is suitable for people with disabilities and other special needs. It involves designing elements that are easy to use for people with varying abilities, and making sure the product is ADA compliant.

Personalization involves allowing users to customize the product or service to meet their needs. This can range from allowing users to change the color scheme of the product, to creating personalized settings for different activities.

User feedback refers to collecting and responding to user feedback. It is important to gather user feedback during development, and use it to improve the product or service as it is being created.

Usability refers to how easy it is for a user to use the product. This includes making sure the product is intuitive to use and making sure that the user can complete tasks without too much difficulty.

❏ Designing a User-Centric Product

Designing a user-centric product involves taking into consideration a few key elements. First, you should consider the beginner user experience – what will the user see when they first open the product? It should be easy to understand and navigate. Consider the visual design as well – make sure the visuals are attractive and engaging.

Navigation is also important – make sure all functions are easy to find. Consider adding a search bar and a help section, to aid users in finding what they need.

Finally, think about the user ability levels – take into consideration age, experience, abilities and other factors that may affect the user experience.

At the end of the day, designing a user-centric product involves considering the user's needs and preferences. Make sure to gather user feedback and use it to improve the product or service. With the right strategies and techniques, you can create an effective product or service that meets the needs of all users.

❑ Identifying User Needs and Ability Levels

It is important to design kiosks with users' needs in mind. To do this, it's necessary to understand their ability levels and the factors that can affect them. Knowing this information will make it easier to create kiosks that are accessible and comfortable for all users.

❑ Researching User Needs

Researching user needs is a key step in designing accessible kiosks. Customer data and online surveys can help in understanding user requirements. This includes their abilities, preferences, expectations, and usage patterns. It's also important to consider the physical and technological environment that the kiosk is going to be used in.

❑ Understanding User Ability Levels

The ability level of users is another important factor to consider when designing kiosks. Age, experience, and disabilities should all be taken into account. It's also important to think about the range of users, not just the average user.

❑ Factors That Affect User Ability Levels

Context and environment can also affect user ability levels. For example, they may be different when the kiosk is in a bright, noisy public space compared to when the kiosk is in a quiet, dimly-lit room. It's important to consider how the physical environment may affect the accessibility of the kiosk, and how the design should be adapted accordingly.

❑ Evaluating User Experience

Evaluating the user experience (UX) should also be done during the design process. This means thinking from the users' perspectives, understanding their needs, and learning from their feedback. Testing the kiosk with a variety of users can provide valuable insight, helping to identify any areas that require improvement.

❑ Understanding User Interface Design

Having a consistent user interface is an essential part of creating a successful kiosk design. A user interface, or UI, is the way a user interacts with and navigates through a kiosk, and making it consistent is key to making it accessible and easy to use. Consistency refers to how the elements of the interface are put together, and how they work in harmony. Without a consistent user interface, kiosks will quickly become confusing and unusable.

The elements of a user interface include things like the layout, color scheme, text size, fonts, and grouping UI elements. It's important to keep these elements consistent - for example, using the same font for titles and headings across the kiosk, or using the same colors to differentiate different parts of the kiosk. Consistency also applies to the way people move through and interact with the interface, allowing users to easily find what they need without difficulty or confusion.

Designing a consistent user interface can be tricky, but it's worth it in the end. To design a consistent UI, it's important to group elements together in a way that makes sense, and to make sure all elements are easy to access and understand. White space is also an important element of UI design – it can help create a sense of order and make the kiosk look more organized. A good rule of thumb is to keep UI elements simple and concise, making them easy to use and understand.

It's also beneficial to look closely at effective UI examples. Examining successful user interface designs on mobile, desktop, and web platforms can provide a wealth of ideas for designing kiosks with a consistent UI. Paying attention to color schemes, navigation bars, and text size can help you create a successful interface.

Creating a consistent user interface is essential for making any kiosk accessible, usable, and successful. With just a few tweaks, kiosks can become more user-friendly and accessible. By understanding the importance of UI design and taking into consideration user needs and ability levels, kiosks can be designed with accessibility in mind.

❏ Determining the Best Interaction Methods

Interaction methods are the way in which a user interacts with a kiosk. The most commonly used methods include gestures, voice commands, and touchscreens. Choosing the best interaction method for a kiosk should take into consideration the user's needs and abilities. It is important to consider what a user needs to accomplish when using a kiosk. Additionally, consider any physical or cognitive disabilities a user may have, as these can affect the way they interact with the kiosk.

When designing an interaction method, it is important to test and optimize it to ensure a positive user experience. The best way to do this is to get feedback from users and use analytics to measure how successful your interaction methods are. Testing the interaction method with users through alpha and beta testing will provide useful insights into the usability of the kiosk. Once a method is chosen, use A/B testing and user feedback to optimize the interaction for users.

It is also important to take into consideration other elements of the user interface when selecting an interaction method. It should be designed to be consistent and easy to use for all users. This includes considering the layout, color scheme, text size, and fonts used in the kiosk. Additionally, consider the beginner user experience, navigation, and visuals to ensure the kiosk is easy to use.

Understanding the user's needs and ability levels is also an important part of developing an effective interaction method. Researching user needs can be done with customer data, online surveys, and other methods. Additionally, factor in the user's age, experience, and any disabilities they may have when designing the interaction method. Consider the context and environment in which the user will be using the kiosk to ensure the best experience. Evaluate the user experience by thinking from the user's perspective. Ask yourself: "What methods would be the most accessible and intuitive for users?"

By understanding the importance of usability in product design, recognizing the need for user-centered design, and identifying users' needs and abilities, you can create an effective and accessible interaction method for your kiosks. Utilize user feedback and analytics to analyze and improve the user experience. Doing so will result in an effective and user-friendly interaction method that can empower people with disabilities.

❏ Analyzing and Improving User Experience

Analyzing and improving the user experience is essential when creating or designing any product, as optimising the user experience can help to make the product more accessible and enjoyable. User experience, or UX, is the overall experience a person has when interacting with any product or service. A good UX should be intuitive, easy to use, engaging, and enjoyable.

When analyzing the user experience of a product, it is important to consider all aspects of how the user interacts and engages with it. This includes considering how the user uses the product, how the product looks, how quickly it responds to user input, how intuitive it is, and how flexible it is when it comes to different types of users. To analyze the user experience, you need to collect data from user feedback, customer surveys, and analytics. This data can give you valuable insight into how people are interacting with your product and where there are areas of improvement.

Once you have analyzed the user experience, you can start to think about strategies for improvement. The strategies you use will depend on what the data has revealed, but some common strategies include content optimization, design changes, or reducing loading times. You might also consider integrating newer technologies or making the user experience more personalised. Additionally, you can use A/B testing and user feedback to refine the product and make sure the changes are beneficial.

When making changes to the user experience, it is important to remember to make it accessible to all types of users. This includes users with disabilities, users of different ages, and users of different abilities. Consider the different types of users and how they might use the product and adapt it accordingly. Ensure that the product is easy to use and understand, and make sure all text is clear and legible.

Finally, it is important to test the user experience once you have implemented the changes. This can be done through A/B testing to see how two different versions of the product compare. User feedback can also help to make sure the changes have improved the product and that the user's experience remains positive.

By analyzing and improving the user experience, you can create products and services that are intuitive, easy to use, and engaging. As a result, your product will be more accessible and enjoyable, and will have a greater chance of success.

❑ Conclusion

This chapter has highlighted the importance of usability in product design. It is essential for designers to incorporate user-centered design principles into their products, taking into account the needs and abilities of their users. This includes developing a consistent user interface, determining the best interaction methods, and analysing and improving the user experience. By doing this, designers can create an intuitive and user-friendly product that will lead to greater user satisfaction.

◣ Examples of Designing for Ease of Use

1. John works in the government sector and he has been designing kiosks for people with disabilities for many years. In order to make the kiosks easier to use, he focused on creating a consistent user interface that was easy to understand. He used a combination of icons, audio prompts, and text instructions that all guided people through the steps they needed to complete.

2. Rachel owns a retail store and wanted to give her customers with disabilities the same shopping experience as everyone else. She designed her kiosks with large,

clear buttons and an intuitive navigation system. She also enabled voice recognition technology so that customers could communicate their needs clearly and quickly.

3. Michael runs a few small kiosks at a local museum. In order to make the kiosks accessible to everyone, he designed them with braille text, headphone jacks, and a large font size. He also included a variety of interactive tools such as a magnifying glass and a colour wheel that allowed people with different vision impairments to interact with the kiosks.

Understand the importance of usability in product design:

1. Research what 'usability' means

2. Learn the different principles of usability

3. Analyse existing kiosk designs to identify usability problems


Recognise the need for user-centered design:

1. Research the concept of user-centered design

2. Consider the needs of your target users

3. Make sure design decisions are based on user needs


Identify users' needs and ability levels:

1. Identify the age, gender and abilities of your target users

2. Research the access needs of users with disabilities

3. Consider the usability of the kiosk for different age and ability levels


Develop a consistent user interface:

1. Brainstorm ideas for an effective interface

2. Design a unified user interface across all areas of the kiosk

3. Test and evaluate the user interface to make sure it works as intended


Determine the best interaction methods:

1. Research different methods of interaction

2. Decide on the most suitable method for your kiosk

3. Make sure the chosen method is accessible to all users


Analyse and improve the user experience:

1. Collect feedback from users

2. Identify areas of improvement in the user experience

3. Incorporate user feedback into the design of the kiosk

◥ A Useful Framework for Designing Ease of Use.


❏ The P.A.C.E. Formula:

1. Personalize: Craft a personalized experience tailored to the user's needs, abilities, and preferences.
2. Accessible: Make sure that the interface is designed with accessibility in mind.
3. Consistent: Create a consistent user interface to reduce confusion and learning curves.
4. Engaging: Provide users with an enjoyable, interactive experience to make the kiosk inviting and entertaining.
5. Evaluate: Analyse user feedback and continually iterate the design to ensure the kiosk remains accessible and easy to use.


❏ Common Pitfalls to Avoid When Designing for Ease of Use

When it comes to designing kiosks for accessibility, many people don't think about the little details that can have a major effect on usability for disabled users. Some of these non-obvious mistakes are assuming that everyone has the same physical abilities, failing to account for sensory impairments, and neglecting to think about the language barrier.

First of all, it's important to remember that not everyone has the same physical abilities. Even though it seems straightforward, many people don't consider whether their design can be used by those with limited range of motion, or who might struggle with fine motor skills. It is important to keep in mind that their hands, arms and other body parts might struggle to maneuver the kiosk, so you'll need to make sure you create an accessible design that meets those needs.

Another non-obvious mistake is to forget about people with sensory impairments. It is easy to forget that people with hearing and/or vision impairments might be using the kiosk, so sight, sound and text should be considered. For example, it's important to ensure that text is large enough for those who have difficulties reading small displays. It is also essential to make sure that visuals are simple and easy to interpret for those with visual impairments, and to provide audio cues for those with hearing impairments.

Finally, language barriers can be an issue when designing kiosks for accessibility. People from different regions or backgrounds might not speak the same language and this can cause difficulty in using the kiosk. It is important to think about the audience and their language preferences, and to provide language options for different user. This can be done by having multilingual support or providing translations of interfaces.

These are some of the non-obvious things people get wrong when designing kiosks for accessibility. Failing to consider these aspects can exclude certain users and limit their ability to interact with the kiosk and access its content. It is important to remember that everyone has different needs and abilities, and to consider these when designing an interface that is accessible and usable for all.

# 11. Creating an Accessible Keyboard Layout

In this chapter, we'll explore how to design an accessible keyboard layout that is comfortable and convenient for all users. We'll look at how to evaluate and test different layouts, how to incorporate features that enhance usability and how to incorporate accessibility into design standards. By the end of this chapter, you'll have the tools and knowledge to create keyboard layouts that are accessible, comfortable and easy to use.

# ◥ Why an Accessible Keyboard Layout is Essential for All Users

The scene is a busy airport. Nervous travelers are hurrying to catch their planes and the air is filled with the sound of excited chatter. In the midst of it all is Jill, a wheelchair user who has come to the airport to fly to her destination. She approaches the kiosk that issues tickets, but finds her way blocked due to the complex design of the keyboard. With only minutes before her flight, Jill is feeling overwhelmed and frustrated; it seems she will never be able to check in on time. But then, a friendly airport employee notices her struggle and upgrades the kiosk to a more accessible keyboard layout. Suddenly the keyboard is easier to use, with larger keys and more intuitive design. Jill smiles with relief and quickly checks in for her flight. With the help of the accessible keyboard design, Jill was able to make it to her flight on time.

Ergonomics plays a major role in designing an accessible keyboard layout. From the spacing of the keys to the size of the keyboard to the angle of the keyboard, ergonomic design can drastically improve the usability and comfort of the interface. By understanding the components of ergonomics, you can design an accessible keyboard layout that is comfortable and efficient to use.

The components of ergonomics are the spatial arrangements, hand movements and other design elements that make up the keyboard layout. Ergonomic design has many benefits, from reducing the risk of injury when typing to increasing efficiency by making it easier to complete a task. These improvements come from having the correct placement of the keys, sufficient key size for the user to easily press them, and an angle of the keyboard that allows for natural hand movement.

When designing an ergonomic keyboard layout, there are several things to consider. For example, the spacing and size of keys play a major role in legibility. The larger the keys, the easier they will be to read, and the further apart they are, the easier they will be to distinguish from each other. Additionally, a good keyboard layout should provide users with tactile feedback to ensure they are pressing the right keys.

When evaluating different keyboard layout options, it is important to do usability testing to ensure the design works for all users. This can involve focus groups, software testing and hardware testing. After assessing the performance data, you can visualize the data to see how the design fares against the objectives to determine a successful design.

Furthermore, when designing an accessible keyboard layout, it is important to have guidelines in place that make it usable and accessible for all users. This includes taking age, physical ability, motor skills and cognitive disabilities into consideration, as well as standard symbols that should be used on keyboards to make them accessible for disabled users. The best approach is to provide alternative inputs for those with disabilities, such as voice recognition and eye tracking. Additionally, it is important to consider installing accessibility software on the keyboard, such as an onscreen keyboard, which provides an alternative for those with physical disabilities.

Finally, enhancing the usability of the keyboard is done by implementing features such as keyboard shortcuts, adjustable layouts and macros. Designing a user-friendly layout can be done by providing personalizable key assignments and tactile feedback. It is also important to ensure consistency in the design by using consistent language, custom keys and a recognizable color scheme.

By understanding the ergonomics of keyboard layout, evaluating and testing different layout options, designing a keyboard that is accessible for all users, implementing features that enhance usability and understanding the importance of color codes and contrast, you can design an accessible keyboard layout that is usable and comfortable for everyone.

❏ Evaluating and Testing Keyboard Layouts

Testing the accessibility and usability of a kiosk's keyboard layout is an integral part of designing a solution that meets the needs of all users. It's important to understand the importance of testing, the tools available to help, and how to evaluate and analyze data to ensure your design is successful.

The importance of testing keyboard layouts cannot be overstated. Usability testing allows you to gain a better understanding of how users interact with the kiosk, and provides insights into how the design can be improved. When evaluating keyboard layouts, focus groups can be used to gain feedback from potential end users, providing valuable insights into areas for improvement.

To help facilitate testing, there are several tools that can be used to evaluate and observe user interactions. Software tools such as heat maps, eye tracking, and motion tracking allow researchers to study how users interact with the kiosk in real-time. Additional hardware tools, such as eye trackers, can also be used to help measure user performance and identify areas of improvement.

When evaluating the success of a keyboard layout, it's essential to set clear objectives and define metrics. For example, track users' completion times, success rates, and errors. Other factors such as user comments, time to complete each task, and user preferences should also be taken into account.

Once testing has been completed, it's important to analyze the performance data to ensure the design meets the objectives. Comparison tests can be used to compare the effectiveness of different designs. This allows developers to make informed decisions about which design is the most successful.

By understanding the importance of testing, the tools available to facilitate testing, and how to evaluate and analyze performance data, developers can make informed decisions about the usability of their keyboard layouts. With the right approach, developers can be sure that their designs will meet the needs of all users, making the kiosk accessible for everyone.

❑ Creating an Accessible Keyboard Layout

Creating an accessible keyboard layout is an essential part of enabling accessibility. It is critically important to design your keyboard layout to be usable and accessible by everyone, regardless of age, physical ability, motor skills and other impairments. To achieve this, the following topics will be covered in this chapter.

❑ Guidelines for Designing an Accessible Layout

Creating an accessible keyboard layout requires understanding of the needs of different users with disabilities, and then designing a layout which accommodates these needs. Common guidelines for designing an accessible layout include maintaining legibility, providing feedback and making the layout easily learnable. It is also important to ensure that the layout is easy to use and navigable, and that users do not have to strain to use it.

❑ Designing a Keyboard That Meets the Needs of All Users

When designing your keyboard layout, it is important to consider the needs of all users, including those with physical disabilities, visual impairments or hearing loss. This includes making sure that the layout is appropriate for various age ranges, users with different types of motor skill impairments and users of different languages. It is also important to consider the use of assistive devices when designing the keyboard, such as voice recognition software and eye-tracking systems.

❑ Standard Symbols Used on Keyboards

When designing a keyboard layout, it is important to think about the symbols used on the keys. Make sure to include symbols that are used by people with disabilities, such as the international symbols for people with disabilities, as well as symbols for alternative characters. Another factor to consider is the use of language symbols, such as those used in different countries or with different alphabets.

❑ Alternatives for Disabled Users

When designing an accessible keyboard, it is also important to consider providing alternatives for users with disabilities. This could include installing voice recognition software on the keyboard, as well as providing onscreen keyboards for users that don't have the ability to use a physical keyboard. Additionally, it is important to provide eye-tracking software for users with visual impairments, as well as alternative inputs for those with dexterity or cognitive impairments.

❑ Installing Accessibility Software on Your Keyboard

In addition to providing alternatives for users with disabilities, it is important to ensure that the keyboard is accessible to users by installing accessibility software. Examples of accessibility software include onscreen keyboards, as well as software which enables users with disabilities to use the keyboard in various different ways. Installing accessibility software can greatly improve the usability of the keyboard for users with disabilities.

By following these guidelines, designers can create a keyboard layout that is accessible for all users. Designing an accessible keyboard layout is essential for enabling accessibility, and is something that all designers should consider when creating their layout.

❏ Enhancing Keyboard Usability

Having a keyboard that is easy to use can help to make your kiosks accessible to all users. There are several techniques you can employ to create a user-friendly keyboard layout and make the most of your design.

The first step is to learn about keyboard shortcuts. Shortcuts are key combinations, such as Ctrl+C or Ctrl+V, that can be used to access certain functions, such as copy and paste. Utilizing these shortcuts can save time and improve efficiency. For example, instead of having to navigate menu options, you can use shortcut key combinations to quickly access the desired command. Additionally, keychains can be used to quickly enter commonly used strings of text with a single key press.

Adjustable layouts can also improve the usability of your keyboard. This allows users to reconfigure the keyboard to suit their needs. For example, you can provide options for different languages and rearrange the location of keys for left-handed users. Additionally, you can add macros to your keyboard, which allow users to trigger a series of keystrokes with a single input.

You should also focus on creating a user-friendly layout. Designing a keyboard the right way can improve the user experience and make the keyboard more accessible. Consider the size of the keys and the amount of space between them. Also, look into tactile feedback options such as audible clicking or vibration. These will provide feedback to the user each time they press a key and make it easier to type accurately.

Consistency is also important when designing a keyboard layout. A consistent design will help users of all abilities find the keys they need. To achieve this, label your keys with standard symbols and use unambiguous language. Additionally, you can provide custom keys for frequently used functions, such as a 'Print' or 'Back' key.

Finally, don't forget about color codes and contrast. A clear color coding system can help users identify errors, as well as improve the overall organization of the keyboard. Choose colors that have a strong contrast to ensure legibility and look for colors that work well together, such as complementary shades. Additionally, avoid colors that could cause colorblindness.

By employing these techniques and focusing on ergonomic design, you can create a keyboard that is highly accessible and easy to use. An accessible keyboard has the potential to make a big difference in the lives of users with disabilities. With the right design, you can provide a comfortable and efficient interface that is powerful and accessible.

❏ Creating an Accessible Keyboard Layout: Color Codes and Contrast

When it comes to designing an accessible keyboard layout, the use of color codes and contrast can play a huge role in making sure it can be used by all users. Color coding and contrast can help to identify errors, can make the keyboard more organized, and can help to improve the overall design. Here's how to make sure you use color codes and contrast correctly when designing an accessible keyboard layout.

When it comes to color codes and contrast, the two important features are color combinations and contrasting colors. Color combinations are the pairing of two or more colors that are used together to create a particular look. Contrasting colors, on the other hand, is a more complicated concept and involves pairing complementary colors that are opposite each other on the color wheel to create a more dynamic look.

It's important to be aware of what colors to use and how to use them. Each color used should have a purpose and should be used in a way that best serves the purpose of the design. When choosing the right colors, categorizing is a great way to organize the colors. Start by selecting a few primary colors and then adding accents of secondary or tertiary colors to create the desired color palette. Additionally, it's important to create patterns of colors that are repeatable and can be used in multiple places.

After choosing the right colors, designing an effective color scheme becomes the next step. The main goal is to create a layout that is usable and accessible by everyone. An effective color scheme will ensure that the color codes and contrast are both visible and easy to understand. Additionally, it's important to avoid color blindness when selecting the colors, as this could potentially cause confusion for users.

Finally, it's important to consider accessibility in the design. An accessible design is a design that can be used and understood by everyone, regardless of ability or experience. When creating an accessible color scheme, it's important to consider the needs of disabled users, such as those with vision impairments. This could include using standard symbols that represent certain functions, as well as providing alternate characters or alternative inputs that are more accessible. Additionally, incorporating accessibility software into the design can help to make the keyboard more usable for more users.

Incorporating color codes and contrast into the design of an accessible keyboard layout is an important part of making sure it can be used by all types of users. By understanding the principles of color codes and contrast, choosing the right colors, designing an effective color scheme, and taking accessibility into account, you can create a keyboard layout that can be used and enjoyed by everyone.

❑ Creating an Accessible Design Standard

When it comes to making kiosks accessible, there is no one-size-fits-all solution. Rather, creating an accessible design standard is key to ensure that all users can access and use the kiosk safely and easily. This means having guidelines and principles in place that can be applied to the design of the kiosk, no matter what the environment or user requirement.

The first step in creating an accessible design standard is understanding the guidelines for an accessible design. This includes knowing how to accommodate different users and how to make the kiosk design easy to learn and use. It is also important to familiarize yourself with the benefits of an accessible design, such as being usable and accessible by everyone regardless of ability level.

The next step is building an accessible design process step by step. This includes conducting research and testing and evaluating different design options. These tasks involve exploring existing design standards, such as those established by international conventions, as well as designing, testing, and documenting the results. Additionally, it is important to create a policy document to outline expectations and standards for all involved.

The final step is establishing your own design standards. This requires internal guidelines, as well as expected outcome measures for specific design goals. It is important to ensure that the policy document and design standards are up to date, and any changes should be communicated to all parties involved in the design process.

Creating an accessible design standard is a necessary step to ensure that all users can navigate and use the kiosk safely and comfortably. Although there are many components to creating an accessible design standard, by following the above steps, you can make sure that your kiosk is designed in the best way possible for all users.

❑ Conclusion

This chapter discussed the importance of designing accessible keyboard layouts to create an environment that is accessible for all users. It discussed the ergonomics of keyboard layout, as well as how to evaluate and test different keyboard layout options. Furthermore, the chapter discussed how to implement features that enhance the usability of the keyboard, such as color codes and contrast, as well as incorporating accessibility into design standards. Overall, this chapter provides guidance on how to make keyboard layouts more accessible for all users.

◼ Examples of Implementing an Accessible Keyboard Layout

Person 1:
Amy was designing an accessible kiosk for a library. She knew it was important to make sure that everyone, no matter their abilities, would be able to use the kiosk. She looked into ergonomics when she crafted the keyboard layout, and she made sure that all the keys were spaced out and easy to press. She also chose colors and contrast levels to make sure users with color vision

deficiency could use the kiosk too.

Person 2:

John was designing a kiosk for his business. He wanted anyone to be able to use it, so he put in the time to research the best keyboard layout. He tested a variety of options, and then implemented a split keyboard design that made typing easier for people with dexterity issues. He also chose a vibrant keyboard backlight and made sure that key labels were easy to read in any lighting.

Person 3:

Jane was creating a kiosk for her city. She needed to make sure that people with different needs could access it. She looked into the principles of universal design and used them to create a keyboard layout that would enable accessibility for everyone. She even created design standards so she could ensure that any future changes to the kiosk would still meet the same accessibility standards.

## ◥ Step-by-Step Guide to Creating an Accessible Keyboard Layout

Stage 1: Understand the ergonomics of keyboard layout
- Learn about the anatomy of keyboards
- Research the effects of different keyboard sizes, depth and key spacing
- Research the possibilities of alternative keyboard layouts
- Become familiar with ergonomics best practices

Stage 2: Evaluate and test different keyboard layout options
- Observe users to understand their typing styles and habits
- Test different set of keyboards with different size and shape
- Introduce alternative layout options to the users
- Gather feedback from the users on the layout options that are most suitable

Stage 3: Design keyboard layouts that are accessible for all users
- Take into account the needs of all users

- Create layouts that are comfortable to use for both experienced typists and those new to computing
- Incorporate ergonomic considerations into the design
- Create a design that minimizes the physical and cognitive effort needed to operate the keyboard

Stage 4: Implement features that enhance the usability of the keyboard
- Incorporate features that allow users to customize their experience
- Utilize proper color codes and contrast to make keys easier to read
- Test the designed keyboard with multiple users for verification

Stage 5: Understand the importance of color codes and contrast
- Identify the importance of color codes and contrast in making keys easier to read
- Understand the significance of using proper colors to avoid any kind of confusion
- Incorporate the use of high contrast colors in the design of the keyboard
- Test the design to make sure that the color codes are easily discernable

Stage 6: Incorporate accessibility into design standards
- Follow accessibility guidelines and standards while designing the keyboard layout
- Understand the needs of people with disabilities and use the guidelines to design an accessible layout
- Make sure the design is tested by people with disabilities for verification
- Incorporate feedback from users with disabilities into the design for higher usability.

## ◣ A Framework for Designing an Accessible Keyboard Layout

The ABC-CDE Framework:

A - Assess - Assess the user's needs and preferences

B - Balance - Balance ergonomics and accessibility

C - Consider - Consider color codes and contrast

C - Customize - Customize the keyboard layout for the user

D - Design - Design the keyboard layout for usability

E - Evaluate - Evaluate the design for usability and accessibility

◥ Avoiding Common Accessibility Missteps When Designing a Keyboard Layout

One of the non-obvious things people often get wrong when designing kiosks for accessibility is failing to take the end user's abilities into consideration. This can range from failing to understand the ergonomic needs of particular users, to providing a keyboard layout that makes it difficult for users to find the keys they need. People often make this mistake because they believe that a 'one size fits all' approach is the answer, but this could not be further from the truth. Every user has different needs and abilities, and it is essential that these are taken into consideration when designing a kiosk.

For example, a person with impaired vision may not be able to see a standard keyboard layout easily, making it hard for them to operate a kiosk. It is therefore important to think about how the keyboard layout can be tailored to meet the needs of this user, such as providing larger keys, or using high contrast colors. Additionally, users with mobility issues may require larger, easier-to-reach keys that are spaced further apart from each other. Taking these needs into consideration when designing a kiosk ensures that the end user will be able to operate it easily and effectively.

Another mistake people often make is failing to test their kiosk designs properly. Testing a kiosk design is essential, as it allows the designer to ensure that their design is functioning correctly and that the user is able to use it successfully. When testing a kiosk, it is important to pay attention to the feedback from users and make changes where necessary. Additionally, it is important to test the keyboard layout for usability, as this can determine whether the user will be able to navigate the kiosk or not.

Finally, another non-obvious mistake people make when designing kiosks is failing to incorporate accessibility standards into their design. Accessibility standards are designed to ensure that all people are able to use technology, regardless of their abilities or disabilities. By following these standards when designing a kiosk, it can ensure that it is accessible to all users, ensuring that they can access the services it provides.

Overall, it is essential to consider the needs of the user when designing a kiosk, as this can make the difference between a successful design and a design that fails to meet the needs of the end user. Additionally, it is important to test the design and incorporate accessibility standards, as this will ensure that the kiosk is usable by everyone. By understanding these non-obvious things, people can ensure that their kiosk designs are accessible to everyone.

# 12. Designing Accessible Non-Text Messages

Discover how to create engaging non-text messages that are accessible to users of all abilities with this chapter. You'll learn about the different types of non-text messages, understand which ones are best for your context, and learn how to design and test them for accessibility. Plus, you'll have the tools and tips you need to ensure your non-text messages are easy to use and understand for everyone. Unlock the power of non-text messages and create more inclusive access with this chapter.

◥ Unlock the Power of Non-Text Messages for Inclusive Access!

This story takes place in a small rural town in the Midwest of America. The main character, Joe, is a local shopkeeper who runs a kiosk in downtown. He wanted to make sure that everyone in the community, including people with disabilities, had access to his services. Joe soon found out that most of his kiosk's user interface was not accessible to those with disabilities.

He was determined to make it accessible though, so he began to research how to design non-text messages that were both accessible and user-friendly. Joe worked hard to understand the principles of universal design and create accessible messages that made sense for the context. He put together a system of non-text messages that allowed for a successful experience for all users, regardless of their abilities.

Joe's hard work paid off and his kiosk became a success. His non-text messages allowed people with disabilities to access his services and feel included in the community. Joe was overjoyed that he was able to remove this barrier and enable accessibility for all.

❏ Understanding Non-Text Alternatives

Providing non-text alternatives to traditional text-based messages can make kiosks more accessible to many people. Non-text messages are visuals, sounds, videos, and animations that can help deliver a message without relying on the user's ability to read or comprehend text. Non-text messages can be used to demonstrate instructions, describe objects or concepts, or convey other important information.

There are several advantages to using non-text messages. Non-text messages can help make a kiosk interface more user friendly, as they can be simpler to understand than text. In addition, non-text messages can be used to provide content in multiple languages, or for those with hearing impairments, or those who find it difficult to read or comprehend text. Non-text messages can be designed to be visually appealing, making them more attractive and fun to use.

Non-text messages can come in many forms, including visual (emoticons, symbols, icons, etc.), audio (sounds, music, speech, etc.), video (clips, videos, etc.) and animation (movement, transitions, etc.).

The type of non-text message used will depend on the context of the kiosk. For example, in public places where there is a lot of noise, audio non-text messages may be more appropriate than visual or animation non-text messages, as they can be heard better. In educational environments, visual non-text messages such as symbols, icons and graphics can be used to help deliver concepts in a more fun and engaging way.

When designing non-text messages, it's important to keep in mind the needs of all users. Non-text messages should be designed to be legible and readable, and easy to understand. They should also include elements of contrast to make them more distinguishable. Colors and textures can be used to add interest and to help make the message stand out. It's also important to consider how the message will be interpreted by those with various disabilities. Non-text messages should be designed to be inclusive of all users, including children, elderly, and those with disabilities.

Testing non-text messages is also essential to ensure that they are readable and can be understood by all users. Before testing, it's important to consider what type of tests are best suited to test the message, as well as which types of users should take part in the tests. Tests may include A/B testing, focus groups, usability tests, and more. Once the tests have been conducted, the results should be evaluated to determine whether the message is suitable and delivers the desired message. Based on the results, changes can be made to the message to make it more readable and understandable. It is also important to monitor the performance of non-text messages over time to ensure they remain accessible, user friendly, and effective.

❑ Non-text Messages for Kiosks

When it comes to designing an accessible kiosk, non-text messages are an important component. Non-text messages provide an alternate way for people with disabilities to interact with the kiosk, and can help make kiosks more user-friendly to all.

Visual non-text messages are perhaps the most commonly used type of non-text messages. These include emoticons, symbols, and icons. Each of these visual messages can easily be understood by most users, and can be used to provide easy-to-understand cues or instructions. It's important to always ensure that visual messages are easily recognizable and easy to understand.

Audio non-text messages are the next type of non-text messages commonly used in kiosks. These include sounds, music, and speech. It's important to use audio messages that are clear, understandable, and loud enough for users to make out easily. For example, you may use a short musical note when a successful task is completed.

Video non-text messages are messages that are displayed onscreen for users to see. These include clips, videos, etc. that can help instruct users on how to use the kiosk. For example, you can create a video that shows how to use the kiosk.

Animation non-text messages are messages that use movement and transitions to help explain a concept onscreen. For instance, you could use animation to show the user where to press a button to start the kiosk.

These non-text messages can help people with disabilities interact with a kiosk, and can help make the experience of using a kiosk easier for everyone. It's important to consider the needs of different users when designing non-text messages, and to always ensure that the messages are legible, readable, and easily understandable. Additionally, it's important to test non-text messages for accessibility and usability, and to monitor the performance of the non-text messages over time.

❑ Designing the Right Non-Text Message for the Right Context

Non-text messages are an important part of making kiosks accessible for people with disabilities. They provide an alternative way to communicate information when text-based messages may be difficult to understand. When considering which types of non-text messages to use in a kiosk design, it is important to consider the context. Different types of non-text messages serve different purposes, and it is important to choose the right one.

The first step in determining which type of non-text message is best suited for a particular context is to consider the audience. Different user groups - such as children, elderly people, and those with disabilities - may have different needs when it comes to non-text messages. For example, graphical icons may be helpful for a child, but may not be as helpful for a person with a cognitive disability. Similarly, animation may be great for conveying a message quickly, but may not be ideal for someone who is blind.

When evaluating the suitability of non-text messages for a particular context, it is also important to consider the nature of the message. Visual non-text messages, such as icons and symbols, are typically used for straightforward messages, such as "Please wait," or "Please select an option from the list." Audio and video non-text messages, such as sound bites, music, and videos, are generally used to convey more complex messages, such as instructions and helpful tips. Animation is often used to convey a more interactive experience, such as showing a demonstration of how to use a particular feature.

If the kiosk needs to be accessible to as broad an audience as possible, it is important to design the non-text messages with the needs of all users in mind. This means that the non-text messages should be designed to be legible, readable, and easy to understand by all users. Visual non-text messages should use contrast to make them easier to read, and should use symbols and icons that are universally understood. Audio and video non-text messages should be audible, clear, and easy to follow. Animation should be used sparingly and be as simple as possible.

The last step in designing non-text messages for a kiosk is to test them for accessibility and usability. Before beginning tests, it is important to consider what types of tests should be conducted, such as A/B testing, focus groups, and usability tests. During the tests, it is important to evaluate the results and identify areas in which non-text messages may need to be improved. After the tests are completed, it is important to monitor the performance and accessibility of the non-text messages over time.

By considering user needs, the nature of the message, and the context, it is possible to create non-text messages that are useful and inclusive for all users. By testing these messages and monitoring the results, it is possible to ensure that the kiosks are accessible and user-friendly for everyone.

❑ Making Effective Non-Text Messages

When it comes to creating modern kiosks that are accessible to everyone, non-text messages are essential. They are visual or auditory signals that enable people with disabilities to interact with the kiosk in the same way that someone without a disability would. Making sure that these non-text messages are effective and easily understandable is key to creating a kiosk that is accessible to all.

When designing your non-text messages, it is important to take into account the aesthetic elements that you are using and make sure they are visually appealing. This helps to create a pleasant user experience and makes it easier for users with disabilities to decode and understand the messages. Choose fonts and symbols that are easy to read and avoid using confusing symbols or cluttered images. The use of contrast is also important, as this helps to make messages more easily readable. Incorporate both light and dark colors and use textures and patterns to draw attention to certain elements.

In addition to aesthetics, effective non-text messages should also take into account the legibility, readability, and ease of understanding for all users. To ensure non-text messages are accessible to all, use a variety of visual cues and symbols to represent different functions. For example, a "play" symbol may be used to indicate a start button or a "stop" symbol may be used to indicate an end button. Aim to make sure that the graphics are simple, recognizable, and make sense within the context of their usage. Pay attention to the size and placement of graphics, as these can also play a role in how easy it is for someone to understand a non-text message.

Finally, it's also important to consider how non-text messages can be inclusive of different user groups. Think about users with visual impairments, hearing impairments, or cognitive impairments and ensure that the non-text messages are designed with their needs in mind. For example, if a kiosk has a volume control, try to make sure that it is large enough to be operated by someone with limited dexterity. Also, consider using symbols and graphics to represent more complex information if they are presented in a way that makes sense to everyone.

By understanding these essential elements and taking the time to design effective non-text messages, you can make sure that your kiosk is accessible to everyone, regardless of their disability.

❑ Designing Accessible Non-Text Messages

Non-text messages, such as visuals, sound, video, and animation, are an important part of making kiosks accessible to everyone. When designing non-text messages, it is important to consider the needs of all users, including the elderly, children, and people with disabilities.

When creating non-text messages, you should consider the context in which the message is being displayed. Different types of messages may be more appropriate depending on the situation, such as emoticons, symbols, icons, sound, music, video clips, and animations. You should also think about the readability and clarity of the messages, as well as their aesthetic appeal.

Using contrast is essential for the legibility of non-text messages. Sufficient contrast is needed for messages to be easily readable, no matter the setting. Other elements like colors and textures can also add interest and engagement to the messages.

When designing non-text messages, it is especially important to make sure they are accessible to all users. You should consider how the messages might be misinterpreted by different people, and how they can be read by individuals using assistive technology. Additionally, the messages should be designed in a way that is comprehensive and can be easily understood.

Before launching messages, it is important to test them for accessibility and usability. A/B testing, focus groups, and usability tests are all valuable ways to evaluate the messages. Testing results should be carefully analyzed and used to improve the messages accordingly. You should also monitor the messages after they have been launched to ensure they remain accessible and serve their purpose.

Designing non-text messages that are accessible and useful to all users requires careful consideration and testing. Involving users from different backgrounds and experiences will help create messages that are more likely to be successful. With the right design, it is possible to create non-text messages that are accessible and accurate for all users.

❑ Testing Non-Text Messages for Accessibility and Usability

Testing non-text messages is key to ensuring that your kiosks are accessible, inclusive and user-friendly. Before testing, make sure to: identify the user groups who will be using the kiosks; determine the objectives of testing; and decide what tests should be conducted.

A/B testing is a great way to evaluate whether non-text messages are effective. This test involves exposing different users to different versions of the same message and measuring their reactions. A/B tests can help you determine which version of your message is the most successful.

Focus groups are also useful for testing non-text messages. This type of testing is done by selecting participants who represent your target audience and having them evaluate different message designs. Focus groups can provide rich insights into the effectiveness of a message.

Usability tests are also a great way to test non-text messages. Usability tests measure how easily users can use a system and how satisfied they are with it. Testing for usability helps you identify potential problems with your message design that can help you improve it.

Once you have conducted these tests, you can use the results to make improvements to your messages. This can include changing the size, color and font of the message text, or even redesigning the whole message. You may also want to think about adding non-text messages, such as symbols and icons, to make your message more accessible and user-friendly.

Finally, when your non-text messages have been tested and improved, you should keep an eye on their performance over time. Regularly monitoring their effectiveness will help you identify any potential problems and determine when it is necessary to make changes.

By conducting these tests and monitoring the results, you can ensure that your non-text messages are accessible, user-friendly and effective. These tests will help you create kiosks that can be used by everyone, making them truly accessible.

❑ Conclusion

In this chapter, we discussed the importance of providing non-text alternatives so that all users have equal access to information. We also learned about the different types of non-text messages, how to identify which type is most suitable for the context, essential elements in successful non-text messages, and how to design and test non-text messages for accessibility and usability. Through these lessons, we have gained a better understanding of how to ensure accessible design for non-text messages.

## ◥ Unlock the Power of Non-Text Messages for Inclusive Access: Examples of Implementation

1. Sarah is a kiosk designer that created a system for people with visual impairments. She designed a series of auditory messages that gave instructions on how to interact with the kiosk in order to access the service. She also designed symbols that used bright colors and clear lines to guide people to the correct button.

2. John is a kiosk designer that created a system for people that are hard of hearing. He designed a series of messages that used sign language. He also incorporated tactile buttons with raised letters to help people find the right button without relying on the sound of the messages.

3. Lisa is a kiosk designer that created a system for people with physical disabilities. She designed a series of messages that used larger font sizes and higher contrast to make the text easier to read. She also designed a joystick that allowed people to click on buttons without needing to use their hands.

## ◥ Step-by-Step List to Unlock the Power of Non-Text Messages for Inclusive Access

Understand the importance of providing non-text alternatives
- Research the different ways that people can interact with technology
- Read about the different types of disabilities and how they might affect using technology
- Understand why non-text alternative is an important part of inclusive design

Learn about different types of non-text messages
- Become familiar with different types of multimedia such as audio, video, images and motion graphics
- Learn about the different types of non-text messages that can be used to make information accessible

Determine what types of non-text messages are most suitable for the context
- Understand the context in which the non-text messages will be used
- Identify the audience and the type of non-text messages they will be most likely to respond to

Identify essential elements in successful non-text messages

- Determine the most effective way to present the non-text messages

- Identify key elements of successful non-text messages such as proper formatting, language and tone

Design non-text messages with the needs of all users in mind

- Research best practices for accessible design

- Develop an appropriate level of complexity for the non-text messages

- Consider how to ensure that the non-text messages are streamlined and easy to understand

Test non-text messages for accessibility and usability

- Perform user testing to ensure that the non-text messages are accessible for all users

- Evaluate how well the non-text messages work on different devices

- Analyze the performance of the non-text messages to ensure they meet the needs of all users.

## ◣ Unlock Inclusive Access with a Step-by-Step Framework

L-A-D-E-T Framework:

1. Listen: Thoroughly Listen to user feedback to ascertain which non-text messages they need.

2. Analyze: Analyze the context and usage scenarios to determine what types of non-text messages should be used.

3. Design: Design non-text messages with the needs of all users and accessibility standards in mind.

4. Evaluate: Test non-text messages for accessibility and usability.

5. Test: Make sure all non-text messages work properly on all platforms.

❑ Common Mistakes to Avoid When Designing Accessible Non-Text Messages

One of the most common mistakes people make when designing non-text messages for accessibility is assuming that people with disabilities are not tech-savvy. This is a major misconception, as individuals with disabilities often have just as much access to technology as anyone else. People with disabilities are just as capable of understanding digital information - sometimes even more so - as those without disabilities.

Another mistake people make when designing non-text messages is assuming that providing the same information in different languages is enough. While providing information in multiple languages is a great start, it doesn't necessarily ensure accessibility. For instance, some languages may not have symbols or pictograms that are required for people with visual impairments. Furthermore, providing only text-based messages in different languages won't guarantee accessibility for everyone; some people with disabilities may actually require more guidance or support when accessing digital information.

It's also important to ensure that any non-text messages are designed in a way that suits the context. People will respond differently to messages depending on the context in which they are presented, so it's important to consider the needs of the user before designing a message. This can include designing messages that are easy to understand, using language that is appropriate to the user's level of expertise, using visual aids to help explain the meaning of the non-text message, and providing alternative messages for users with different needs.

Finally, it is important to test any non-text messages to ensure that they are accessible and usable for everyone. This involves testing the messages for clarity, comprehension, and usability with an array of participants. Testing will allow you to gain insight into how your message is perceived by different users and how to make it more accessible.

In conclusion, designing non-text messages for accessibility requires more than just providing the same message in different languages. It's important to consider the needs of the user, design messages that suit the context, and test them to ensure they are easy to understand and use. If these steps are followed, you can be sure that your non-text messages are accessible to all.

# 13. Designing for Visually Impaired People

Designing kiosks for visually impaired people is an important part of creating an accessible environment. In this chapter, you'll learn how to make sure your kiosk is usable for people with visual impairments. We'll discuss strategies for using appropriate contrast and text size, audio descriptions, and tactile feedback. You'll also learn about non-visual cues, video magnification, and creating materials in various formats for accessibility. By reading this chapter, you'll get the tools needed to make sure your kiosk is truly accessible and welcoming to all users.

◥ Why Accessibility Matters: Designing for Inclusivity and Welcoming Everyone

On a busy day in the city, Molly was trying to catch the bus to her doctor's appointment. She had been blind since she was a little girl and, even with her white cane, it was still hard to find her way around. As she approached the bus stop, she could feel her anxiety growing as she struggled to feel for the bus stop sign. Suddenly, she heard a voice coming from the kiosk next to her. It was the automated voice guide system that was installed just a few weeks ago. She breathed a sigh of relief as the system helped her identify which bus to take and when it was coming right away. By using the kiosk, Molly was able to make it to her doctor's appointment on time without any trouble. Thanks to the accessible kiosk design, she was able to navigate the city with greater confidence and independence.

❑ Designing with Appropriate Contrast and Text Size

When designing a kiosk, it is important to keep accessibility in mind. One aspect of accessibility is the contrast between elements on the kiosk's interface and the size of the text. Low contrast and poor text size can make it difficult for people who are visually impaired to use the kiosk, so it is essential to carefully consider how these elements are designed.

❑ Why is Contrast and Text Size Important for Accessibility?

High contrast between elements on the screen and text size large enough for the user to read without difficulty are essential for making kiosks more usable for people with visual impairments. Low contrast can make it difficult for the user to differentiate between different elements. Small text can be difficult to read and make it impossible for some people with visual impairments to use the kiosk.

❑ Guidelines for Choosing Optimal Contrast and Text Size

When designing an accessible kiosk, it is important to choose an appropriate contrast between elements on the screen and an appropriate text size.

The Web Content Accessibility Guidelines (WCAG) provide guidelines for what is considered an acceptable contrast ratio. The minimum acceptable contrast ratio is 4.5:1. Darker text on a lighter background or lighter text on a darker background is recommended.

Choosing an appropriate text size is equally important. The WCAG recommends a minimum text size of at least 16pt. However, some users may be more comfortable with a larger size than this.

❑ Testing Contrast and Text Size for Accessibility

Once you have chosen the contrast and text size for your kiosk, it is important to test it to ensure accessibility. One way to do this is to use a color contrast analyzer tool to test the contrast between elements on the screen. This will let you know if the contrast is high enough for accessibility.

It is also important to test the text size to ensure it is readable. To do this, it can be helpful to have someone with visual impairments test out the kiosk to determine if the text size is comfortable enough for them to read.

❑ Conclusion:
Creating an accessible kiosk involves thoroughly considering elements such as contrast and text size. It is important to meet the minimum standards set by the Web Content Accessibility Guidelines. Testing the contrast and text size on the kiosk is essential to ensure accessibility. With the right design, a kiosk can be accessible to all users, regardless of visual acuity.

# Creating Audio Descriptions for Kiosks

Audio descriptions are an important part of making kiosks accessible to people with vision impairments. Audio descriptions are verbal descriptions that are added to a kiosk interface to provide additional information that may be difficult for a person with vision impairments to understand.

When creating audio descriptions for kiosks, it's important to ensure that the audio descriptions are clear and easy to understand. The audio should be recorded in a calm, steady tone and should be loud enough to be heard clearly. It's also essential to include information that is relevant to the kiosk interface and what the user is seeing on the screen. For example, if the user is looking at an image of a shopping cart, the audio should explain what type of shopping cart it is.

When creating audio descriptions, it's also important to consider what to include in the audio description. It's essential to include any features that a person with vision impairments may not be able to see, such as colors or symbols. Audio descriptions should also provide an explanation for any complex buttons or controls the user needs to interact with, such as a visual slider or a checkbox. Additionally, audio descriptions should be brief and concise to avoid confusing the user.

The benefits of adding audio descriptions to a kiosk interface are numerous. By providing audio descriptions, users with vision impairments will be able to better understand what is on the screen and interact with the kiosk more effectively. Additionally, audio descriptions can help to increase accessibility for other users, such as people with cognitive disabilities.

When creating audio descriptions for kiosks, there are some examples of effective audio descriptions that can be used. One example is including brief descriptions of images or visuals on the kiosk interface, such as explaining what is shown in a photograph or video. Another example is providing instructions on where to place objects in the kiosk, such as when the user needs to place an item within a certain area of the kiosk. Lastly, audio descriptions should always provide an explanation of the available options or features the user can interact with.

In order to make kiosks accessible to people with vision impairments, including audio descriptions is essential. By providing a comprehensive and clear audio description, users will be able to understand and easily interact with the kiosk. It's important to ensure that audio descriptions are concise and relevant to the screen, as well as providing an explanation of any complex features or buttons present. Additionally, by making use of some examples of effective audio descriptions, you'll be able to ensure your kiosks are accessible and user-friendly.

❑ Voice Control and Tactile Feedback: Designing for Visually Impaired People

Voice control and tactile feedback are two important aspects of making your kiosks more accessible to visually impaired people. Both technologies aim to improve the user experience by making it easier for them to interact with the kiosk.

Voice control technology allows users to control the kiosk by speaking into it. This means they don't need to use any physical buttons or touch the display. In this way, visually impaired people can interact with a kiosk without having to worry about not being able to see the buttons or touch the display.

The tactile feedback feature allows users to feel when they press a button. This is important because it helps the user know when their input has been registered. This is particularly helpful for visually impaired people as it allows them to interact with a kiosk without having to look at the display.

Integrating voice control and tactile feedback features into your kiosk design can be a challenge, but it pays off in the end as it allows more people to access and use your kiosk. To do this, you need to make sure that your kiosk is compatible with the necessary hardware and software. After you've done that, you need to properly program the kiosk so that it can interpret the user's voice commands and tactile input correctly.

Examples of successful implementations of voice control and tactile feedback into kiosks include ATMs, ticketing machines and even public art installations. These kiosks all have features that allow users to control their features with voice commands and tactile feedback, allowing visually impaired people to fully participate and interact with them.

By incorporating voice control and tactile feedback features into your kiosk design, you'll be able to make your kiosk more accessible and usable for visually impaired people. This will help you create an inclusive experience for everyone, regardless of their visual abilities.

❑ Non-Visual Cues for Visually Impaired People

Non-visual cues such as alarms, vibrations, and audio tones can be incredibly useful for people who are visually impaired. Non-visual cues can help alert users to important events and changes, notify them of tasks that need to be completed, or provide feedback on their interactions with a kiosk.

When it comes to designing for visually impaired people, non-visual cues play an important role in making sure that the kiosk is accessible to all. Incorporating non-visual cues into the design can be a simple and effective way of providing equal access to all users.

❏ What are Non-Visual Cues?

Non-visual cues are cues that use other senses such as sound, touch, or vibration to convey information. Alarms and audio tones are two common examples of non-visual cues; they can be used to alert users to changes, as well as indicate completion of tasks. Vibrations can also be used to indicate events, such as when a button is pressed or when a task is completed.

❏ Examples of Non-Visual Cues

Alarms and audio tones are some of the most common forms of non-visual cues. However, there are other forms that can be used as well. Low frequency tones can be used to provide a warning when users are in close proximity to a kiosk, and tactile feedback in the form of vibrations can be used to indicate when a button is pressed or when a task is completed. Additionally, tactile feedback in the form of a raised or textured surface can be used to give users a point of reference when navigating a kiosk.

❏ Benefits of Including Alarms and Other Non-Visual Cues

Non-visual cues can be a great way of ensuring that a kiosk is equally accessible to all users, regardless of their level of visual impairment. By providing non-visual cues in the form of alarms, audio tones, vibrations, or tactile feedback, you are making sure that the kiosk is accessible to all users. Additionally, non-visual cues can be more effective than visual cues in some cases; for example, alarms and audio tones are more effective at conveying information to users who may be in another room or have limited vision.

Including non-visual cues in the design of a kiosk can be a simple yet effective way of providing equal access to all users. By incorporating alarms, audio tones, vibrations, and tactile feedback, you can ensure that the kiosk is accessible to visually impaired people. These non-visual cues can provide users with the information they need to interact with the kiosk and provide an equal level of access to all users.

❑ Designing for Visually Impaired People

Visually impaired people can often face barriers when using kiosks, which is why it is important to ensure any kiosk designed is accessible to this demographic. Video magnifiers and screen magnifiers are two important tools that can help make kiosks more accessible to visually impaired people.

Video magnifiers allow users to zoom in and out on images, which is beneficial for those with low vision who may have difficulty seeing details or reading fine print. Video magnifiers can also be adjusted to different color contrasts to make images easier to read. Screen magnifiers, on the other hand, allow kiosk users to enlarge the entire screen and make it easier for those who have difficulty seeing small fonts.

When choosing a video magnifier or screen magnifier for your kiosk, it is important to consider the needs of your target audience. Those with limited mobility may benefit from a video magnifier with a larger field of view, while those with limited peripheral vision may need a more precise view. Additionally, consider the size and shape of the magnifier, as well as the color contrast adjustments the device offers.

Once you have selected the right video magnifier or screen magnifier for your kiosk, it is important to properly install and test the device to ensure it is working correctly. It is also important to ensure the device is compatible with the kiosk and that the interface is optimized for users with visual impairments. For example, it is beneficial to increase the font size and add a "zoom" button to the kiosk screen, as this can make it easier for visually impaired people to read and navigate their way around the kiosk. Additionally, adding text-to-speech capabilities is useful for those with vision impairments who may have difficulty reading text on the kiosk's display.

By taking the time to choose the appropriate video magnifier or screen magnifier for your kiosk and to ensure it is properly installed and optimized, you can make your kiosk more accessible to those with visual impairments. By doing this, you can open up the kiosk to a larger audience, making life easier for those with vision impairments and empowering them to be more independent.

❑ Creating Accessible Materials

Having accessible materials is an important part of ensuring accessibility at kiosks. By creating materials in various formats, such as Braille, audio, and large print, individuals with disabilities will have access to the information they need.

❑ Types of Formats
Braille is a system of raised dots that are used to represent letters and numbers. It can be read by people who are blind or have low vision. Audio is a spoken version of the text that can be accessed by people with visual impairments or low literacy levels. Large print is text that is easier to read because it is larger than regular text. It can also be used by people with low vision.

❑ Tips for Creating Materials
When creating materials in these various formats, it is important to design them with accessibility in mind. Make sure that the text is easily legible and that the audio is easy to understand. When creating large print materials, use a font size that is easy to read.

❑ Benefits of Creating Materials
Creating materials in various formats can provide a range of benefits. It can make it easier for individuals with disabilities to access and understand the information they need. It can also help increase the overall accessibility of the kiosk, as it allows for a wider range of users to access the information.

❑ Guidelines for Creating Materials
When creating materials in various formats, it is important to adhere to certain guidelines. For example, make sure that the text size and contrast is consistent across all formats. When creating an audio version, ensure that the information is presented in a clear, concise manner and that the speaking speed is not too fast. For Braille materials, ensure that the text is translated correctly into the dots and dashes of the language.

Creating materials in various formats can be a great way to make kiosks more accessible. By adhering to the guidelines set out above, you can ensure that individuals with disabilities will have access to the materials they need.

❏ Conclusion

In this chapter, we discussed how to design for visually impaired people. Specifically, we discussed the importance of designing with appropriate contrast and text size, adding an audio description to the kiosk interface, incorporating features such as voice control and tactile feedback, including non-visual cues such as audio alarms, providing video magnifier and/or screen magnification, and creating materials in various formats for accessibility. By taking these steps, organizations can ensure that their products and services are accessible and inclusive for all users.

◣ Real-Life Examples of Accessibility in Action

1. Sarah, a fashion designer, wanted to make it easier for people with low vision to shop for her clothing. She added bright contrasting colors to the kiosk background and increased the text size for easy reading. She also included audio cues when customers searched for items, to help them find what they were looking for. Finally, she added a video magnifier to the kiosk, so that people with low vision can zoom in on the items they're looking for.

2. John, a restaurant owner, wanted to make sure that people with hearing impairments could access his services. He included an audio description when customers interact with the kiosk, so that they understand what they need to do. He also added tactile feedback, so customers know when they have interacted with the kiosk correctly. Finally, he added audio alarms that notify staff whenever new orders have been placed.

3. Rachel, a museum curator, wanted to ensure that her materials were accessible to everyone. She created materials in different formats, including audio, large print, and Braille. She also included voice control and video magnifiers on the kiosk interface, so that people with visual impairments could interact with the kiosk easily.

## ◥ Step-by-Step List of Real-Life Examples of Accessibility in Action

❑ Designing for Visually Impaired People

- Ensure there is an appropriate contrast with the kiosk's color scheme and font size
- Make sure information included on the kiosk's interface is not only visual, but also has an audio description
- Introduce features such as voice control and tactile feedback to aid in navigation
- Utilize non-visual cues such as audible alarms to provide feedback
- Include a video magnifier or a screen magnification option for those who may not be able to see the kiosk's display
- Provide materials in various formats to make them accessible to everyone, such as braille or large print

❑ A Practical Framework for Accessible Design: Real-Life Examples

The EAZY Framework -
Evaluate contrast and size
Audio description
Zoom capacity
Yell out notifiers

## ◥ Common Mistakes to Avoid When Designing for Visually Impaired Users

Kiosk design is a complex process and typically involves many steps. As such, there are a number of potential pitfalls and errors that can occur during the design process. One of the most common mistakes people make when designing kiosks is failing to consider accessibility. Kiosks are intended to serve a wide range of users, but if the design fails to accommodate individuals with disabilities, those users may not be able to access the kiosk and its services.

Another mistake that is often made is failing to create an interface that is both visually and audibly accessible. People with different types of disabilities may rely on various methods to interact with the kiosk, and if the kiosk lacks the proper interfaces, then these individuals may not be able to use the kiosk at all. For example, people who are blind or have poor vision may rely on audio descriptions to understand the kiosk's interface. Therefore, it is important to include an audio description to ensure accessibility.

Similarly, people who are deaf or hard of hearing may rely on non-visual cues to interact with the kiosk. Without the proper cues, these individuals may not be able to understand what the kiosk is asking or telling them. Therefore, it is important to include features such as audio alarms or tactile feedback to ensure accessibility.

Finally, people with cognitive disabilities may rely on various formats to access the kiosk. For example, some individuals may need a simplified text format to understand the kiosk's content. Therefore, it is important to create materials in various formats that are easily accessible to all users.

It is important to remember that kiosks are designed to serve a wide range of users and should be designed accordingly. By taking into consideration accessibility and the needs of individuals with disabilities, the design process will be easier and more effective. Failing to consider accessibility can lead to mistakes that can potentially prevent individuals with disabilities from accessing the kiosk and its services. Therefore, it is important to always keep accessibility in mind when designing a kiosk to ensure that all users can gain the benefits of the kiosk.

# 14. Making Your Kiosks Accessible to Hearing Loss

In this chapter, you'll explore how to make your kiosks and interactive technology accessible to people with hearing loss. You will learn how to improve the transparency and accessibility of audio feedback, and how to incorporate visual cues to assist users. You will also learn about different types of hearing loss and how they affect the way people use technology. You'll gain an understanding of how audio amplification systems can be used to improve the accessibility of audio instructions. With the strategies you learn here, you can create a more accessible kiosk experience, allowing users with hearing loss to enjoy the same convenience and enjoyment as any other user.

# ◥ Why Accessibility is Important for People with Hearing Loss

It was a summer day in a small town. Marley is a young girl who is hard of hearing, and today she was out with her family to get something to eat. She was excited to be out with her family, but as they approached the door of the restaurant, her heart began to sink. She knew how much trouble she was going to have to go through to order her food with the big, intimidating kiosk.

Marley's parents tried their best to help her navigate the touchscreen, but it was useless. The audio instructions were too low for her to hear and the visuals weren't helpful either. No matter how hard they tried, Marley was at a loss.

But then something wonderful happened. Another customer noticed the struggle Marley and her family were having and pointed out that the kiosk had a hearing aid loop. With the help of the loop, Marley was now able to hear the instructions clearly. She placed her order with confidence and went inside the restaurant to enjoy her meal with her family.

This story illustrates the importance of making sure kiosks are accessible to people with hearing loss. Making kiosks accessible can open up amazing opportunities for people with hearing impairments, and create a stress-free experience.

## ❑ Making Your Kiosks Accessible to Hearing Loss

Hearing loss is a disabling condition that affects more than 500 million people worldwide. It can prevent them from understanding and participating in their environment, and it makes it difficult to access technology. In this section, we will cover information about the causes and types of hearing loss, how to diagnose it, and how to make technology accessible for people with hearing impairments.

Hearing loss is caused by damage to the structures of the ear, which can occur naturally as people age, or be caused by exposure to loud noise, infections, or side-effects of certain medications. It is also possible to be born with hearing loss.

There are three major types of hearing loss: sensorineural, conductive, and mixed. Sensorineural hearing loss is caused by damage to the inner ear structures, while conductive hearing loss is caused by damage to the outer or middle ear. Mixed hearing loss is the combination of both.

Diagnosing hearing loss is done through hearing tests and audiograms. During a hearing test, an audiologist will use a series of pure-tone signals to determine the levels at which a person can hear sound. Audiograms measure a person's hearing level across all frequencies.

People with hearing loss use assistive technology like hearing aids and assistive listening devices to help them access and understand sound in their environment. Technology can also help by monitoring sound levels, providing speech recognition, and offering vibration alerts for people with hearing impairments.

When designing audio feedback for kiosks, it is important to make sure that the audio is easy to understand. This can be done by providing clear speech, using tone and volume, and avoiding sudden changes in sound. It is also important to keep the complexity of audio information low, by avoiding long words and other confusing audio information.

It is also important to provide audio instructions on kiosks to make them easier to use for people with hearing impairments. These audio instructions should be provided in a clear, consistent manner and should also be easy to understand. They can be provided through a voiceover, sound recordings, or even text-to-speech technology.

Audio amplification systems can also be used to make kiosks accessible to people with hearing loss. These systems amplify sound and other audio sources to make them easier to hear and understand. They can range from simple devices that have one microphone and one speaker, to more complex systems with multiple microphones and speakers.

In addition to audio instructions, it can be helpful to provide visual cues as well. This can include sign language, colour codes, gestures, flashing lights, and tactile feedback. Visual cues can help make it easier for people with hearing loss to access and understand the information on kiosks.

Making kiosks accessible to people with hearing loss is an important part of universal design. Following the advice outlined in this section will make it easier for people with hearing impairments to access and use kiosks.

❑ Making Your Kiosks Accessible to Hearing Loss

For people with hearing impairments, technology can be an invaluable resource. It can help people with hearing impairments to understand audio feedback and access audio instructions more easily, enabling them to use kiosks with less difficulty. In this section, we will explore the tools and techniques used by people with hearing impairments, and the strategies that can be used to make kiosks more accessible.

❑ Common Tools Used

Hearing aids and assistive listening devices are the most common tools used by those with hearing impairments. Hearing aids are small electronic devices that are placed in or around the ear to amplify sound. They work by amplifying sound waves that enter the ear, making it easier for the person to understand and interpret audio feedback. Assistive listening devices are similar to hearing aids, but instead of amplifying sound waves that enter the ear, they use external speakers to transmit audio signals directly to the person with the hearing impairment.

❑ How Technology Can Help

Advanced technology has enabled improved monitoring of sound levels and improved accuracy of speech recognition. This means that voice activated systems can be used to control kiosks. In addition, many hearing impaired people now have access to devices that can interpret dialogue and speech as text. This means that audio instructions can be presented as text on the kiosk display, making them easier to understand.

❑ Challenges with Using Technology

Despite the potential benefits that technology can provide, there are still challenges with using technology. The cost of the necessary devices can be prohibitive, and there is a risk that the devices may be incompatible with the kiosk. In addition, audio instructions are more difficult for hearing impaired people to interpret than text instructions, so it is important to provide clear audio instruction, and to support these instructions with visual cues where possible.

By understanding the tools used by those with hearing impairments, and the challenges associated with using them, you can start to craft strategies that can help make your kiosks more accessible. In the next section we will explore strategies for providing clear audio feedback and for enhancing the accessibility of audio instructions.

❑ Making Audio Feedback Easier to Understand

Audio feedback is an important tool for making kiosks accessible to those with hearing impairments. While this feedback can be beneficial, it also needs to be clear and easy to understand in order for it to be effective. This means that the audio feedback should be simple and straightforward, and should be presented in such a way that it can be easily interpreted. To do this, there are a few key strategies that should be taken into consideration.

First and foremost, it is important to make sure that the audio feedback is presented in a way that is easy to understand. This means using clear speech, and avoiding long and complex words or phrases. It is also important to ensure that the tone of the audio feedback is appropriate, as a too high or too low voice can be hard to understand. Additionally, it can be helpful to adjust the volume of the audio feedback, so that it is neither too loud nor too soft for the user.

Another important aspect of making audio feedback easy to understand is to make sure that it is consistent. This means that the audio feedback should remain the same throughout the user's experience, with no sudden changes in sound. This makes it easier for the user to orient themselves and understand the audio feedback without having to endure any unexpected surprises.

Finally, it is important to minimize the complexity of the audio information. This means avoiding long words or phrases, and providing concise instructions that can be easily understood by the user. Additionally, it is best to divide the instructions into smaller chunks that can be easily comprehended by the user. This will help the user follow the instructions more easily and quickly.

By following these strategies, it is possible to make audio feedback easier for those with hearing impairments to understand. With clear and consistent audio feedback, it is possible to empower users by providing them with the necessary information and instructions needed to use kiosks with ease.

❑ Making Your Kiosks Accessible to Hearing Loss

Providing audio instructions for people with hearing impairments is an important step in making your kiosks accessible and user-friendly. Audio instructions can make the experience of interacting with the kiosk easier and more enjoyable for those with hearing impairments. There are several techniques you can use to ensure your audio instructions are accessible and provide a positive user experience.

❑ Benefits of Audio Instructions

Audio instructions provide an easy way for people with hearing impairments to understand the instructions they are being given. By providing audio instructions, users will have increased understanding of what to do and where to go on the kiosk, allowing them to easily interact with the computer in a comfortable manner. Audio instructions also provide a sense of independence and can help build confidence in those with hearing impairments.

❑ Techniques for Creating Audio Instructions

When creating audio instructions for your kiosk, it is important to consider the type and length of instructions you are providing. Generally, instructions should be short, concise and easy to understand. You should also focus on providing simple instructions that don't require too much focus and/or concentration. Audio instructions can be recorded by voiceovers or sound recordings, but be sure to use a voice that is natural, clear and not too robotic.

❑ Optimizing Audio Instructions

When creating audio instructions, be sure to avoid background noise that can muffle the instructions and make them difficult to hear. Additionally, use pitch and tone to emphasize certain instructions. For example, using a higher pitch at the end of instructions can help make the instructions stand out. Finally, use a friendly and reassuring tone that conveys the message and ensures users understand what the instructions are asking them to do.

By considering the tips and techniques outlined in this chapter, you can make your kiosks more accessible for people with hearing impairments by providing them with clear audio instructions. Taking the steps to make your kiosks as accessible as possible for all users can ensure a positive user experience and lead to increased loyalty and satisfaction.

❑ Understanding Audio Amplification Systems

Audio amplification systems are a powerful tool to make it easier for hearing impaired people to interact with machines. These systems provide a way to increase the clarity and volume of sound, making it easier for those with hearing impairments to understand what is being said through the device.

An audio amplification system is an electronic system that takes audio inputs, such as voices, and boosts the level of the signal so that it is louder and clearer. It can be used by people with hearing impairments to hear more clearly and to increase their understanding of what is being said through the machine. There are two main types of audio amplification systems: Speech to Text, which converts speech into written words, and Speech to Speech, which converts speech into spoken words.

The benefits of audio amplification systems are immense. For those with hearing impairments, the increased clarity and volume of sound can make a huge difference in their ability to interact with the machine. This can improve communication and comprehension, enabling them to interact with the machine more easily. Audio amplification systems can also help to increase awareness of speech, making it easier to understand what is being said.

Audio amplification systems can also benefit people who are deaf or hard of hearing. By providing an audio signal that is louder and clearer than the signal they normally receive, they can be more easily able to understand what is being said. This can help them to be more easily engaged with the device, making it easier for them to interact with it.

Finally, audio amplification systems can provide a greater level of clarity for anyone who is trying to interact with the machine. The improved sound makes it easier for everyone to understand what is being said, which can increase its usability for everyone.

When designing kiosks, it is important to consider how audio amplification systems can benefit users with hearing impairments. By providing them with an increased level of clarity and volume, it is possible to make the machine more accessible and easier to use. It is also important to ensure that the design of the audio amplification system is optimized, so that the audio signal is clear and consistent. Finally, it is important to consider the use of visual cues to accompany the audio instructions, as this can help to make them easier to understand.

❑ Making Your Kiosks Accessible to Hearing Loss

When it comes to making your kiosks accessible to people with hearing loss, it's important to incorporate visual cues in addition to audio instructions. Visual cues can help supplement audio instructions and make it easier for people with hearing impairments to understand and follow along.

When utilizing visual cues, use strategies such as sign language, different colors and symbols. Sign language is useful for providing direction to someone with hearing impairments, whereas colors and symbols are helpful for enhancing audio instructions. When using colors, make sure the colors are in contrast with the background to make sure they stand out. When utilizing symbols, there should be fewer symbols than colors to avoid too much confusion.

The benefits of providing visual cues to accompany audio instructions are immense. Visual cues can help people with hearing impairments better understand and access information with ease. Additionally, it aids communications as people with hearing loss can quickly understand instructions. Furthermore, visual cues can help remove any ambiguity, making it easier for people with hearing impairments to comprehend instructions.

Examples of visual cues include gestures, flashing lights, and tactile feedback. Gestures are helpful for indicating intent, such as a thumbs up indicating approval. Flashing lights can be used to indicate when exactly to provide input in an interactive session. Lastly, tactile feedback can be used for simple instructions, such as gently shaking an arm to indicate a request for assistance.

However, there are some challenges associated with using visual cues. For example, people with impaired vision may not be able to make out the visual cues. In such cases, additional measures such as tactile feedback might be necessary. Additionally, if too many visual cues are used in a short period of time, it could lead to confusion. Therefore, it's important to carefully consider the types of visual cues you are going to use and how often you are going to use them.

Making your kiosks accessible to hearing loss can be challenging. However, by leveraging strategies such as sign language, colors, symbols, and tactile feedback, you can make it easier for people with hearing impairments to understand and access information with ease.

❏ Conclusion:

This chapter provided a summary of the strategies to make kiosks more accessible to people who are hearing-impaired. It covered the basics of hearing loss, the use of technology by people with hearing impairments, and how to improve audio feedback and accessibility. Additionally, the chapter discussed methods to enhance the use of audio instructions, such as the use of audio amplification systems and visual cues. By following these strategies, businesses can improve their kiosks to better support their customers who are living with hearing loss.

◥ Examples of Accessibility Solutions for People with Hearing Loss

1. Maria had a kiosk in a train station which she wanted to make accessible to people with hearing loss. She started by researching the different types of hearing loss and how people with hearing loss use technology. Once she had this knowledge, she was able to create an interface that was easy for people with hearing loss to use. She added an audio amplification system and provided visual cues to reinforce audio instructions.

2. Mark created a kiosk in a retail store that was accessible to people with hearing loss. He used speakers that amplified audio instructions and added visual cues to help people with hearing loss better understand the instructions. He also made sure to make all the audio feedback as clear as possible.

3. Jane installed a kiosk in a bank that was accessible to people with hearing loss. She made sure that the audio instructions were easily understandable, and that they were properly reinforced with visual cues. She also added an audio amplification system so that the audio instructions were clear and easily understandable for people with hearing loss.


## ◣ A Step-by-Step List of Accessibility Solutions for People with Hearing Loss

1. Understand the basic types of hearing loss:
 - Learn about the different types, causes and symptoms of hearing loss
 - Research how hearing loss can affect a person's ability to understand audio instructions and feedback

2. Be familiar with how hearing impaired people use technology:
 - Research the devices, services and technology available to help people with hearing loss
 - Explore different methods of audio communication used by hearing impaired people

3. Learn how to improve the transparency of audio feedback:
 - Learn how to make audio feedback clear and understood by people with hearing loss
 - Understand how to adjust the volume level, pitch and tone of audio feedback to be more understood by people with hearing loss

4. Know how to enhance the accessibility of audio instructions:
 - Become familiar with speech recognition technology and how it can help people with hearing loss
 - Learn the different techniques to make audio instructions easier to understand for people with hearing loss

5. Be familiar with the use of audio amplification systems:
 - Research the different types of audio amplification systems available
 - Find out the pros and cons of each system and determine the best one to use for a given situation

6. Consider the use of visual cues to accompany audio instructions:
 - Learn how to add visual cues to audio instructions to make them easier to understand
 - Explore the different tools available for creating visuals for audio instructions


## ◤ A Framework for Accessibility Solutions to Help People with Hearing Loss

Amplify Accessibility:

A formula to make kiosks accessible to people with hearing loss:

1. Recognize the Types of Hearing Loss
2. Create Transparent Audio Feedback
3. Utilize Audio Amplification Systems
4. Provide Visual Cues with Audio Instructions


## ◤ Common Mistakes to Avoid When Designing Kiosks for People with Hearing Loss

Many people make the mistake of thinking that designing an accessible kiosk is all about adding features like audio instructions and visual cues. However, there are many other non-obvious elements that come into play when designing kiosks for people with disabilities.

One mistake is overlooking the importance of usability. When designing kiosks, many people focus solely on making the kiosk accessible without considering whether it is actually user-friendly. Usability is critical for all people, but especially for those with disabilities.

Another mistake is not considering the needs of people with multiple disabilities. Many times, designers will focus only on accommodating one type of disability, without taking into consideration the broader needs of people with multiple disabilities. This can lead to kiosks that are inaccessible to a large number of users.

People often also underestimate the value of proper research. When designing kiosks, it is important to conduct user research and focus groups in order to understand the needs of all user types. Research can help identify potential obstacles and help designers make decisions about what features will work best for each user group.

A fourth mistake is not understanding that certain features can be beneficial for all users, not just those with disabilities. Many times, people think of accessibility as something that is only relevant to people with disabilities, when in actuality many features that are designed to be accessible can improve the experience of all users.

Finally, many people overlook the importance of testing. Testing is essential in order to make sure that the features of a kiosk are accessible, usable, and beneficial for all user types. Testing should be done throughout the design process in order to identify and fix any potential issues.

Designing accessible kiosks is an important task that requires careful consideration of the needs of all users. By considering the mistakes discussed above, designers can ensure that their work is beneficial to all users.

# 15. Designing for Dexterity Challenges

This chapter will provide you with the tools to help make your kiosks accessible to users with dexterity challenges. You will learn about the various types of dexterity challenges, and how to design features and user interfaces that are conducive to those challenges. Additionally, you will discover the importance of alternative input devices and feedback mechanisms that can help make kiosks more accessible to users with dexterity challenges. By reading this chapter, you will gain the knowledge and expertise to create an inclusive, user-friendly environment for all of your customers.

# ◣ Why Your Kiosk Design Matters for Users with Dexterity Challenges

The setting is a busy, bustling grocery store checkout line. Mary is a cashier, and is about to help her next customer. Upon approach, she notices a blind customer, using a cane to orient himself. Mary quickly realizes that the store has not provided any of the usual adaptive tools, so she takes it upon herself to assist him. She takes the customer to her own kiosk, which is conveniently equipped with a voice-enabled interface and audio feedback. Mary then gently and patiently helps the customer with his purchase, speaking slowly and clearly to guide him through the process. Despite the challenge, the customer is successful in completing his transaction. Mary's thoughtfulness and empathy had enabled accessibility for this customer, and he is overwhelmed with gratitude. Mary had sought to ensure that all shoppers feel welcome and, no matter their abilities, are able to make their purchases.

## ❑ Designing for Dexterity Challenges

When it comes to designing kiosks, it's important to recognize the variety of dexterity challenges that people may face. Dexterity challenges can range from fine motor impairments that make it difficult to press small buttons, to gross motor impairments that can make it difficult to access the kiosk's functions. By understanding the different types of dexterity challenges, you can make better design decisions that make it easier for everyone to use your kiosk.

The most common type of dexterity challenge is a fine motor skill impairment. This is a difficulty with small, precise movements of the body, including the fingers, hands, and wrists. Fine motor skill impairments can make it difficult to press buttons on the kiosk's screen, type on the keyboard, and use the mouse. Examples of medical conditions that can cause fine motor skill impairments include cerebral palsy, muscular dystrophy, and carpal tunnel syndrome.

Another type of dexterity challenge is a gross motor skill impairment. This is a difficulty with larger, overall body movements. Gross motor skill impairments can make it difficult to move the kiosk's keyboard or mouse, as well as to reach the kiosk's buttons and switches. Examples of medical conditions that can cause gross motor skill impairments include multiple sclerosis, spinal cord injury, and Parkinson's disease.

The impact of dexterity challenges on kiosk usage can be significant. For example, a user with a fine motor skill impairment may struggle to press a small button on the kiosk's screen, while a user with a gross motor skill impairment may struggle to reach the kiosk's controls. Fortunately, there are design techniques you can use to make your kiosks more accessible for people with dexterity challenges. By recognizing the features of a kiosk that can affect people with dexterity challenges, you can create an interface that works for everyone.

❑ Designing for Dexterity Challenges

Are you looking to create a kiosk that can be used by those with dexterity challenges? The key to success is understanding the various difficulties that those with decreased dexterity can face related to kiosk design. It's also essential to evaluate the efficacy of current features, analyze how well the design works for those with dexterity challenges, and suggest alternate features based on user feedback and research.

When it comes to kiosk design, the screen size is an important factor to consider when accommodating those with dexterity challenges. It may be difficult for those with physical impairments to reach all areas of the screen, so it is important to ensure the screen is not too small. Additionally, the keyboard layout should be kept straightforward and simple, as complex keyboard layouts can be difficult for those with physical impairments to navigate. Furthermore, providing users with the ability to adjust the font size is beneficial for those who struggle to read the text on the screen.

The usability of the kiosk should also be tested and evaluated for those with dexterity challenges. This includes considering the ergonomics of the design, as well as how easy the kiosk is to use. Additionally, users should be able to easily adjust and customize the kiosk to suit their needs. It is essential that users are able to access the buttons and menus without difficulty. Additionally, the kiosk should be designed to be accessible, even when using alternative input methods or alternative control options.

Alternative input methods and alternative control options are important tools when designing a kiosk for those with dexterity challenges. These include voice commands, motion detection, trackballs, joysticks, and touchscreen technology. It is important to ensure that whatever option is chosen is compatible with the kiosk's operating system and is easy to understand and use.

Additionally, applications and buttons should be designed with enlarged characters and text that is easy to understand.

Finally, it is important to implement the proper feedback mechanisms for those with dexterity challenges. This should include audio and visual feedback, error messages that are meaningful, haptic feedback, and confirmations and alerts. This will help users maintain awareness and provide the proper feedback.

By understanding the difficulties that those with dexterity challenges face, implementing proper feedback mechanisms, and utilizing alternative input methods and control options, it is possible to create a kiosk design that is accessible and user-friendly. Doing so will enable those with disabilities to use kiosks with ease, granting them the same accessibility and convenience that able-bodied people have come to expect.

❑ Designing for People with Dexterity Challenges
Designing a kiosk that is accessible to people with dexterity challenges is an essential part of creating a user-friendly product. By understanding the differences between dexterity challenges, recognizing features of a kiosk that can impact usage, and developing user interfaces that meet the needs of the users, you can make a kiosk that is usable for all.

The principles of universal design provide an effective framework for designing the kiosk. These principles focus on providing a design that is accessible for all users. In order to create an effective user interface, you need to consider the use of color, font size, and layout. Utilizing tools and techniques such as keyboard overlays and alternate keyboards can help make the kiosk more accessible. It is also important to create content that is easy to understand, particularly for people with dexterity challenges. Testing the usability and accessibility of the kiosk can help to ensure an effective design.

Touchscreen technology can provide effective solutions for people with dexterity challenges. Using larger buttons and simplifying the user interface can help make the kiosk easier to use. Additionally, alternative input methods such as voice commands and motion detection can be used to control the kiosk. It is essential to consider the needs of the users when choosing an appropriate alternative input device, such as cost and portability.

Feedback mechanisms are an important part of making the kiosk accessible. Audio feedback, visual cues, and haptic feedback can all be used to provide useful feedback to the user. Short, understandable messages should be used to maintain awareness and provide helpful information. Confirmations and alerts can also be used to maintain awareness and provide helpful feedback.

Designing for people with dexterity challenges requires understanding the different types of challenges and the impact they can have on kiosk usage. By recognizing the features of a kiosk that can affect people with dexterity challenges, learning how to design an effective user interface, considering the use of alternative input devices, and implementing feedback mechanisms, you can create a kiosk that is accessible to all.

❑ Designing User Interfaces for People with Dexterity Challenges

Creating a user interface that is both accessible and user-friendly is not just important for people with low dexterity, but for everyone. It's all about making sure that the kiosk is usable by as many people as possible. One of the most important aspects of creating user friendly interfaces is understanding the importance of feedback. This can include anything from error messages to haptic feedback, allowing the user to understand what is happening, no matter their level of experience. It is also important to utilize alternative control methods for those with dexterity challenges. This could include voice commands, motion detection, and so on.

Touchscreen technology is becoming more and more important in kiosk design and it should be utilized effectively. This includes enlarging buttons and installing features such as zoom-in and zoom-out. It is also important that the kiosk is able to recognize different pressure levels, as some users may have trouble applying the right amount force. Consider the use of alternative input devices as well, such as trackballs and joysticks. This is especially important when cost and portability are considered.

Finally, it is important to ensure that feedback mechanisms are implemented correctly. This includes exploring audio feedback, visual cues, and meaningful feedback messages. This can be as simple as having a confirmation message for every button press, or creating alerts for unusual situations. Feedback also plays an important role in informing the user that their actions were successful, as this is particularly important for users with dexterity challenges. By paying attention to all of these aspects, it is possible to create a user interface that is accessible and user-friendly for everyone.

□ Alternative Input Devices for Dexterity Challenges

For people with dexterity challenges, the use of alternative input devices is a must to give them the access they need to use kiosks. Alternative input devices can range from simple trackballs to sophisticated voice recognition systems. But, before choosing an alternative input device, it's important to consider the user's needs to ensure it's suitable and cost-effective.

When selecting an alternative input device, the first thing to consider is the user's needs. Different types of alternative input devices may be necessary depending on the user's specific dexterity challenge. Trackballs, touchpads, and joysticks are some of the most common types of alternative input devices. Trackballs are small hand-held devices that can be used to move the cursor onscreen. Touchpads are flat, pressure-sensitive pads that control the cursor in the same way as a mouse but use the user's finger instead of a mouse. Joysticks are stick-like devices that allow the user to control the cursor by pushing, pulling, and twisting the stick.

Once the appropriate device is chosen, it's important to consider the cost and compatibility of the device. Cost is an important factor when selecting an alternative input device as these devices can be expensive and the cost may add up quickly depending on the number of devices needed. It's also important to make sure the device is compatible with the kiosk's operating system, as some devices are designed to work only with specific operating systems.

Finally, it is important to understand the importance of providing feedback to users with dexterity challenges. Without feedback, these users may not be aware of errors or may simply give up, so it's important that the kiosk provides appropriate and meaningful feedback when necessary. Feedback can come in the form of audio, visual, or haptic feedback, depending on the user's needs. Audio feedback can be used to alert the user of an error or to provide feedback when a task has been completed. Visual cues can be used to indicate the user's progress or to provide additional information if necessary. Haptic feedback can also be used to provide users with useful information without the need for them to look at the screen.

By taking the time to understand the different types of alternative input devices, considering the user's needs and the cost of the device, and implementing appropriate feedback mechanisms, you can ensure that people with dexterity challenges have the access they need to use kiosks to their fullest potential.

❏ Feedback Mechanisms for People with Dexterity Challenges

When designing kiosks for people with dexterity challenges, it is essential to consider the importance of feedback. Correct and clear feedback can help users make informed decisions and ensure their kiosk experience is seamless. It is important to understand the different types of feedback approaches and how to make them meaningful to the user.

Audio feedback is the most common type of feedback for people with dexterity challenges. Audio feedback can be personalized for the user, and it can be used to give information on the success or failure of an action taken. For example, an alert sound can be used to inform users when an action or instruction has been accepted. Audio feedback also allows users to receive information without looking away from their task.

Visual cues are another form of feedback that can be used to inform users of their actions. This type of feedback is less intrusive than audio feedback and can be used to provide succinct information. Visual cues can be used to indicate the status of a command or to provide a response to an action taken. For example, a checkmark icon can be used to indicate a successful task.
Error messages are a form of feedback that can help users understand why an action has failed. Error messages should be concise and written in a language that is easy to understand. By providing clear information about why an action has failed, users can identify any problems and make the necessary adjustments.

Haptic feedback is another approach to providing feedback. This form of feedback uses physical sensations to provide users with information. For example, a vibration or a click can be used to notify users that their action has been accepted. Haptic feedback can be especially beneficial for people with vision impairments, as it can provide information without relying on visuals.

Confirmations and alerts are another type of feedback that can be used to provide users with information. Confirmations can be used to confirm a user's actions and alerts can be used to provide users with important information or to warn them of potential problems.

Overall, feedback is an integral part of designing an accessible kiosk for people with dexterity challenges. By understanding the different types of feedback and how to implement them effectively, kiosks can be made more accessible and user friendly. Clear and concise messages can help users make better decisions, while providing the kiosk with information about their needs and preferences. By making sure that the kiosk is able to provide appropriate feedback, users can be empowered and enabled to access important information in a hassle-free manner.

❑ Summary

This chapter has provided insight into how to design for people with dexterity challenges, including how to recognize the features of a kiosk that can affect them, how to develop appropriate user interfaces, and how to implement feedback mechanisms. In conclusion, understanding the different types of dexterity challenges and developing user interfaces with alternative input devices can help reduce the potential difficulties that people with dexterity challenges can face when using a kiosk.

### ◥ Examples of Kiosk Design Solutions for Users with Dexterity Challenges

1. Victoria runs a grocery store that offers a touchscreen kiosk for customers. She wanted to make sure that people with dexterity challenges could easily use the kiosk, so she added a big button on the side of the kiosk that allows customers to confirm their selections with a single press. She also added a headphone jack and audio instructions to the kiosk so customers can easily hear the instructions instead of interpreting written ones.

2. Jordan was working on a kiosk project for a museum. He realized that people with dexterity challenges sometimes have difficulty using trackpads and keyboards, so he added a foot pedal to the kiosk. This allows visitors to control scrolling, typing, and clicking with their feet so they can still navigate the kiosk without having to rely on their hands.

3. Charlotte runs a clothing store that uses touchscreen kiosks for customers to place orders. To make sure people with dexterity challenges can easily use the kiosks, she added a voice recognition system that allows customers to make their selections verbally. This way, customers only need to say what they want and the kiosk will automatically select it for them.

◥ Step-by-Step List of Kiosk Design Solutions for Users with Dexterity Challenges

Understand the different types of dexterity challenges:
- Research the different types of dexterity challenges
- Learn about how different disabilities can affect the use of a kiosk
- Understand what adaptations can be made to make a kiosk accessible

Recognize the features of a kiosk that can affect people with dexterity challenges:
- Identify different features of a kiosk (keyboard, screen, buttons, etc.)
- Evaluate how these features impact users with dexterity challenges
- Understand what adaptations can be made to accommodate these users Learn how to design for people with dexterity challenges:
- Research different design principles that can be used to create an accessible kiosk
- Develop a user-centered design that is tailored to the needs of people with dexterity challenges
- Learn how to create accessible user interfaces

Develop appropriate user interfaces for people with dexterity challenges:
- Create alternative user interfaces that are tailored to users with dexterity challenges
- Research what features are important for accessibility for users with dexterity challenges
- Identify different elements that can be used to create an accessible user interface

Consider the use of alternative input devices for people with dexterity challenges:
- Determine what type of alternative input device would be suitable for people with dexterity challenges
- Research what features should be included in the input device
- Identify which input devices can provide the best user experience

Implement feedback mechanisms for people with dexterity challenges:

- Research what type of feedback mechanisms are available
- Learn how these feedback mechanisms can help people with dexterity challenges
- Design and implement feedback mechanisms that can be used to enhance the user experience.

## ◤ A Framework for Kiosk Design Solutions for Dexterity Challenges.

The 4 D's Framework:

1. Detect: Identify the user's dexterity challenges.
2. Design: Create a user interface that takes into account dexterity challenges.
3. Devices: Consider alternative input devices for people with dexterity challenges.
4. Feedback: Implement feedback mechanisms for people with dexterity challenges.

## ◤ Avoiding Common Mistakes When Designing for Dexterity Challenges

When designing kiosks with accessibility in mind, one of the most common mistakes people make is assuming that people with disabilities have the same needs and preferences as those without. Many people incorrectly assume that all people with disabilities require the same type of design and interfaces, which is simply not true. Everyone is different and may have vastly different needs and preferences when it comes to the layout, look, and feel of a kiosk. As such, designers must take the time to properly understand and listen to the needs of their target audience.

Another mistake people often make when designing for accessibility is failing to consider the limitations of some assistive technologies. For example, voice recognition systems may be great for people with certain disabilities, but they may be completely useless to people with others. It is important to weigh the pros and cons of any technology and to consider how it will interact with the people intended to use it.

Another common mistake is underestimating the power of feedback mechanisms. People with disabilities may not always know what they need, so it is important to provide feedback options such as sound notifications or visual cues to help them understand when they have successfully completed an action. These feedback mechanisms can be tied to various assistive technologies as well, to ensure that people with disabilities have the best possible experience engaging with a kiosk.

Finally, a mistake people often make is failing to understand the importance of universal design. Universal design is the idea that designs should be created with a wide variety of disabilities in mind, not just with a specific group in mind. This means that designs should incorporate features that allow for everyone to use the kiosks, regardless of their ability. When done correctly, this approach can ensure that everyone feels welcome when engaging with the kiosk, regardless of their disability.

Unfortunately, many people underestimate how difficult creating accessible kiosks can be. Whether it's failing to understand the different needs of different types of disabilities or not providing enough feedback mechanisms, there are many common mistakes people make in relation to designing kiosks with accessibility in mind. By understanding these mistakes and taking the time to develop an appropriate design, kiosk designers can ensure that everyone, regardless of their disability, can access and use the kiosks they create.

# 16. Designing for Cognitive Disabilities

Cognitive disabilities can have a major impact on a person's ability to interact with kiosks. Designers need to strive to create an interface that provides access to all users, regardless of their cognitive abilities. This chapter will discuss how to design kiosks that are specifically tailored to meet the needs of those with cognitive disabilities. We will explore what types of cognitive disabilities are common and how they affect the way kiosks are used. We will also discover the best methods for designing a kiosk interface that is accessible and user-friendly for those with cognitive disabilities. Finally, we will look at how to test your design for effectiveness and make sure that it meets the needs of users with cognitive disabilities. By exploring these topics, we hope to empower designers to create interactive kiosks that are accessible to all.

It was a hot summer afternoon in Chicago's Logan Square. A mother and her daughter, who had autism and a cognitive disability, walked up to a nearby kiosk to buy tickets to a show. The mother had to help her daughter understand the kiosk, but with its cluttered interface and confusing layout, it was hard to figure out. As each moment passed and the line of people behind them grew, frustration began to set in.

Then, the mother noticed a 'help' button. She clicked it and was relieved to find that it kept the same language, graphics, and design elements across the entire kiosk to assist her daughter and make it easier to understand. The mother and her daughter were able to buy the tickets they needed quickly and easily.

This true story serves as an example of how designing kiosks with the needs of users with cognitive disabilities in mind can make life easier. By using consistent language, graphics, and design elements, the kiosk was user friendly for people with cognitive disabilities and enabled them to get the tickets they needed.

❑ Understanding Cognitive Disabilities

Cognitive disabilities are impairments that affect the way individuals think, learn, and remember. They can be developmental, acquired, or part of a neurological disorder. People can have more than one type of cognitive disability, and some may be more subtle than others.

To understand cognitive disabilities, it is important to consider the different types and what they mean. Developmental disabilities are diagnosed early in life and can include conditions such as autism, dyslexia, or Down syndrome. Acquired disabilities typically occur later in life as a result of an injury, illness, or aging. They may present as Alzheimer's disease, dementia, or a traumatic brain injury. Cognitive impairments are typically seen as deficits in memory, learning, or other areas of cognition, such as understanding language.

Common examples of cognitive disabilities include dyslexia, autism, Alzheimer's, and dementia. Dyslexia is a learning disability that is characterized by difficulty in reading, writing, and spelling.

People with autism have difficulty with social interactions and communication, and they often display repetitive behaviors. Alzheimer's is a degenerative neurological disorder that affects memory and other cognitive functions. Dementia is also a neurological disease, but it is characterized by impaired memory and judgement as well as a decrease in cognitive abilities.

Understanding the effects of cognitive disabilities is important for designing kiosks that are more accessible for this population. People with cognitive disabilities often have difficulty navigating menus, understanding text, and interacting with the system. They may also experience cognitive overload when presented with too many options or not enough guidance. By making the user interface easier to use and understand, people with cognitive disabilities can better interact with kiosks.

Designers must also consider how cognitively impaired users are likely to interact with the kiosk. It is important to include design strategies that improve the user experience, such as intuitive navigation, simplified menus, and visible feedback. Additionally, it is crucial to make the interface easier to comprehend, by using dynamic icons, large buttons, and shortcuts. Reducing cognitive overload is also important in making kiosks more accessible for users with cognitive disabilities.

Including accessibility features as part of the design is also essential for users with cognitive disabilities. Assistive technologies, such as voice recognition, text-to-speech, and screen readers, can help people with cognitive impairments interact with the kiosk. It is important to identify the right accessibility features that are appropriate for the target group. Additionally, designers should conduct research and testing with users with cognitive disabilities to ensure the design meets their needs. Surveys, interviews, and focus groups are all important in getting feedback from these users.

By taking into account the needs of cognitively impaired users during the design process, designers can create more accessible and effective kiosks. Understanding the various types of cognitive disabilities, and the effects they have on users, is the key to designing and building a kiosk that is welcoming and easy to use. With the right strategies and design processes, designers can create kiosks that enable people with disabilities to more fully access and enjoy the experience of using technology.

❏ Understanding the Effects of Cognitive Disabilities

People with cognitive disabilities may face several challenges when using kiosks. These challenges can relate to visual impairments, difficulty understanding menus, cognitive overload, and confusion about how to interact with the system. People who have cognitive impairments often experience poorer performance on tasks that require quick decision making, memory, and judgment.

Visual impairments may cause difficulty in identifying important elements on the kiosk's interface, like buttons, menus, and icons. For people with cognitive disabilities, understanding menus can be a challenge, and they may have difficulty understanding text-based instructions or images. Cognitive overload can result from a complex user-interface or too many on-screen elements at the same time. Furthermore, individuals with cognitive impairments may find it difficult to understand even simple instructions or commands.

It is important to remember that each person's situation is unique, and the effects of cognitive disabilities will depend on the individual's condition. As a designer, it is important to be attentive and understand the challenges that users with cognitive disabilities may face. Some of the most commonly used strategies to improve the user experience include using intuitive navigation, simplifying menus, and providing visible feedback.

In addition, it is important to be aware of how cognitive disabilities can affect a user's ability to interact with the kiosk. For example, having a better understanding of how users with cognitive impairments interact with the system can help shape the design to fit their needs. Additionally, using alternate input methods like voice recognition and speech input can help create a more accessible interface and reduce the impact of cognitive disabilities.

Finally, it is important to test the kiosk design with users with cognitive disabilities before deploying it. This will help to identify any problems and make sure that the interface is effective and easy to use for everyone. Gathering feedback from users with cognitive disabilities through usability testing, surveys, and focus groups can be beneficial in designing an interface that meets the individual needs of users.

By following these design practices, you will be able to effectively create a kiosk design that is accessible and accommodating to people with cognitive impairments. Understanding the effect of cognitive disabilities on user experience is invaluable in creating an interface that is both comfortable and easy to use.

❑ Designing for Cognitive Impairments

When designing a kiosk interface, it is important to consider the needs of users with cognitive disorders. Cognitive impairments, such as developmental or acquired disorders, can make it difficult or impossible for some users to navigate and interact with a kiosk in the same way as someone with no cognitive impairment. Designers must take the time to understand the common types of cognitive impairments and their effects on kiosk navigation, so that they can make adjustments to their interface design to create an accessible and user-friendly kiosk experience.

❑ Understanding the Common Types of Cognitive Disabilities

Before beginning the design process, it is important to understand the different types of cognitive disabilities and the various impairments associated with each one. A cognitive disability is any impairment that affects a person's ability to process information, problem-solve, or interact with their environment in some way. Common types of cognitive disabilities include developmental ones such as Autism Spectrum Disorder, dyslexia and Attention Deficit Hyperactivity Disorder (ADHD), acquired ones such as Traumatic Brain Injury and stroke, and neurological diseases such as Alzheimer's and dementia. Common types of cognitive impairments associated with these disabilities include memory deficits, learning disabilities, difficulty understanding text, difficulty comprehending information, and difficulty with spatial orientation.

❑ Be Aware of the Effects of Cognitive Disabilities on Using Kiosks

Cognitive disabilities can have a major impact on how someone interacts with a kiosk. Common challenges faced by users with cognitive disabilities when using kiosks include trouble understanding menus and navigating the system, difficulty understanding text, poor performance, and confusion on how to interact with the system. This can lead to reduced usability and a frustrating experience when using the kiosk.

❑ Learn How to Adjust the Interface to Suit the Needs of Users with Cognitive Impairments

In order to create an accessible and user-friendly kiosk experience for all users, it is important for designers to take steps to adjust the interface for those with cognitive impairments. This can be done by using design strategies such as intuitive navigation, simplified menus, as well as visible feedback and clear instructions. Designers can also make the interface easier to understand by utilizing dynamic icons and large buttons. To reduce cognitive overload, designers can also incorporate shortcuts and limit the number of options presented.

❑ Develop a Design Process That Considers the Needs of Cognitively Impaired Users

In addition to adjusting the interface design for cognitively impaired users, it is also important for designers to create a design process that considers their needs. This includes researching the target audience, gathering data on existing products, and testing with real users. User interviews and focus groups are also important in identifying user requirements and understanding how cognitively impaired users interact with a kiosk. Prototypes and mock-ups can also be used to test the user interface and ensure that it meets the needs of cognitively impaired users.

❑ Include Features to Support Users with Cognitive Disabilities

Designers can also incorporate accessibility features into their kiosks in order to improve usability and make them easier to use for those with cognitive disabilities. Examples of such features include text-to-speech and voice recognition, as well as screen readers and other assistive technology. Designers should use surveys and user interviews to help identify the right accessibility features for their kiosks.

❑ Test Your Design with Users with Cognitive Disabilities to Ensure Effectiveness

The best way to ensure that a kiosk interface is effective and accessible for users with cognitive disabilities is to test it with these users. Testing can help designers discover any problems and issues that may not be apparent when testing with someone without cognitive impairments. Techniques and tools such as usability testing and A/B testing can be used to test the interface, as well as surveys and user interviews. By testing with cognitively impaired users, designers can address user needs and make sure that the kiosk is effective and accessible for all users.

❑ Designing for Cognitive Disabilities

When designing a kiosk for users with cognitive disabilities, it is important to keep some key considerations in mind. Designing an accessible interface tailored to the needs of cognitively impaired users can help make the kiosk more inclusive and user-friendly.

❑ Analyzing and Understanding User Requirements

The first step in the design process is to gain an understanding of the requirements and needs of the target user group. To do this, you should conduct thorough research into the target audience, gathering data on the type of cognitive disabilities they may have, their common challenges and needs, and their preferred ways of interacting with technology. User interviews and focus groups can provide invaluable insight into their experiences with kiosks and possible usability issues.

❑ Designing the Interface

Once you have gathered the necessary data and insights, you can begin designing the interface of the kiosk. Some of the design strategies to consider while designing the interface include intuitive navigation, simplified menus and fewer options to reduce cognitive overload, visible feedback, and clear instructions. Additionally, you can design dynamic icons and large buttons to make the kiosk easier to understand and use.

❑ Creating Prototypes

Creating prototypes is an important part of the design process. Prototypes help you to quickly spot any issues in the interface, as well as fine tune the design and make sure that the user experience is seamless and easy. When creating prototypes, you should consider user flow diagrams, mock-ups and other visual elements to give an accurate representation of the interface design.

❑ Including Accessibility Features

Including accessibility features such as voice recognition and text-to-speech can be beneficial for users with cognitive disabilities. These features can help to make the kiosk more user-friendly and accessible by allowing users to interact with the kiosk in different ways. Identifying the right accessibility features for users with cognitive disabilities can be done by conducting surveys and interviews with users.

❑ Testing with Cognitively Impaired Users

Testing the kiosk design with cognitively impaired users is essential to ensure its effectiveness. Using techniques such as A/B testing, usability testing and user interviews can provide valuable feedback on the design and help you identify any problems that need to be addressed. Gathering feedback from users with cognitive disabilities can help to refine the design, as well as ensure that the kiosk meets their specific needs.

By following the above steps and using the right design strategies, you can design a kiosk that is accessible and user-friendly for people with cognitive disabilities. With the right design, the kiosk can become a valuable tool for making life easier for people with cognitive impairments.

❑ Including Accessible Features

When designing a kiosk for people with cognitive disabilities, it is important to consider the accessible features that can be included. Accessible features provide a way to enable disabled users to interact with the kiosk and to use it as comfortably and conveniently as possible.

One of the most useful accessible features is voice recognition, which allows disabled users to use voice commands to interact with the kiosk. This can be particularly helpful for people with cognitive disabilities, who may struggle with cognitive overload when navigating through menus and understanding text.

Text-to-speech is another important tool for those with cognitive impairments, as it allows them to quickly and easily understand text that would otherwise be difficult for them to read. Quality text-to-speech technology can make it easier for those with cognitive disabilities to interact with a kiosk and to understand the information displayed.

Screen readers are also a useful accessibility tool for those with cognitive disabilities, as they allow disabled users to interact with a kiosk even if they are unable to interact with the screen. Screen readers use auditory feedback to provide instructions and information to the user and can be a great way to make a kiosk more accessible and user-friendly.

Finally, speech input is a great way to make a kiosk more accessible for those with cognitive disabilities. Speech input allows disabled users to interact with the kiosk using voice commands, enabling them to use it easily and comfortably.

When designing a kiosk for those with cognitive disabilities, it is important to consider the accessible features that are available and to select those which are most likely to be useful for the target audience. Accessible features such as voice recognition, text-to-speech, screen readers, and speech input can all help to make a kiosk more accessible and user-friendly for those with cognitive impairments.

❑ Testing for Accessibility in People with Cognitive Disabilities

Testing your interface designs with people who have cognitive disabilities is an important step to ensuring that it meets their needs. This process helps you to identify any potential issues that might make the kiosk difficult to use, so you can make improvements and create an accessible user experience.

Testing can take many forms, from A/B testing to usability testing. A/B testing is a process by which two versions of a design are compared to assess which performs better, and this can be used to test an interface with users with cognitive disabilities. Usability testing, meanwhile, involves observing people using a product to check that they are able to complete tasks quickly, easily, and accurately.

The most effective way to get feedback from people with cognitive disabilities is through focus groups. This involves bringing people together to discuss their experiences of using a product or service, and gives them the chance to provide direct feedback on your design. Interviews and surveys are useful for collecting data from a wider audience, and can also be used alongside focus groups for a more comprehensive assessment.

When conducting testing, it's important to remember that every user is different. People with cognitive disabilities will have different needs and abilities, so it's important to consider individual needs and adjust the test accordingly. For example, if the user is visually impaired, you should adjust the testing environment accordingly, such as providing an alternative input device or adjusting the font size.

Finally, when considering feedback, it's important to take into account the user's overall experience, rather than focusing on the specifics of their disability. People with cognitive disabilities are just like other users, and they should be treated as such. The aim should be to create a design that is accessible to all.

Testing your kiosks with users who have cognitive disabilities is an essential part of the design process. It allows you to identify any issues before they become problems, and to create an interface that is tailored to the needs of all users. By following the tips outlined in this chapter, you can ensure that your kiosks provide a smooth, accessible experience for everyone.

❑ Conclusion

This chapter explored how to design kiosks with cognitive disabilities in mind. The common types of cognitive disabilities and their effects on using kiosks were discussed. It was also highlighted that a design process should be used to ensure that the needs of users with cognitive impairments are met. This includes including features to support users with cognitive disabilities and testing the design with users with cognitive disabilities to ensure effectiveness. Ultimately, this chapter provided an understanding of how to design effective kiosks for an audience with cognitive disabilities.

# ◥ Examples of Accessible Kiosks for Cognitively Disabled Users: Unlocking Equal Opportunity for All

Person 1: Maria creates kiosks to help people with cognitive disabilities stay connected to friends and family. She designs the user interface to be as simple as possible and adds font sizes that can easily be adjusted. She also adds in options for voice or video calls so that users can communicate in the way they feel most comfortable.

Person 2: Harry designs kiosks to help people with cognitive disabilities access employment resources. He creates an interface with large buttons, so it's easier to press them and selects a font with easily readable characters. He also adds an audio mode, so users can listen to instructional material.

Person 3: Samantha develops a kiosk for people with cognitive disabilities to access educational materials. She adds in a simple menu and large text, as well as a library of videos that explain topics in an engaging way. She also includes a mode where users can hear the material with audio narration.

# ◥ Step-by-Step List of Accessible Kiosks for Cognitively Disabled Users

Understand the Common Types of Cognitive Disabilities:

1. Do research to learn more about the various types of cognitive disabilities.

2. Identify which types of disabilities you need to consider when designing a kiosk.

Be Aware of the Effects of Cognitive Disabilities on Using Kiosks:

1. Research and understand the common challenges faced by those with cognitive disabilities when using kiosks.

2. Identify which types of cognitive disabilities could negatively affect a user's kiosk experience.

Learn How to Adjust the Interface to Suit the Needs of Users with Cognitive Impairments:

1. Research interface designs that are suitable for users with cognitive disabilities.

2. Identify the components that need to be adjusted for users with cognitive disabilities.

3. Consider how changes to the interface could make it easier for users with cognitive disabilities to use the kiosk.

❑ Develop a Design Process that Considers the Needs of Cognitively Impaired Users:
1. Review your current kiosk design process and identify opportunities for improving it to meet the needs of cognitively impaired users.
2. Brainstorm design strategies that could better accommodate users with cognitive disabilities.
3. Develop and implement an updated design process to include strategies in support of users with cognitive disabilities.

❑ Include Features to Support Users with Cognitive Disabilities:
1. Identify features that could help to reduce cognitive load on users with cognitive disabilities.
2. Research existing products that use similar features to gain an understanding of how they are implemented.
3. Consider how these features could be incorporated into the kiosk design.

❑ Test Your Design with Users with Cognitive Disabilities to Ensure Effectiveness:
1. Identify potential users with cognitive disabilities who can provide feedback on kiosk designs.
2. Develop user testing scenarios that can give insight into how users with cognitive disabilities interact with and perceive the kiosk design.
3. Organize and execute a user testing session with users with cognitive disabilities and take note of their feedback.

◤ Unlock The Benefits of Accessibility: A Step-By-Step Framework for Designing Kiosks for Cognitively Disabled Users

The A.U.C.E Formula:
Acknowledge - Understand the common types of cognitive disabilities
Unify - Be aware of the effects of such disabilities on using kiosks
Configure - Adjust the interface to suit the needs of users with cognitive impairments

Empower - Develop a design process that considers the needs of cognitively impaired users and test your design with users with cognitive disabilities to ensure effectiveness.

### ◣ Common Mistakes in Designing for Cognitive Disabilities

Many people believe that designing kiosks to be accessible to people with cognitive disabilities isn't important. This mistake occurs because people don't think of cognitive disabilities when they consider accessibility. They assume that people with cognitive disabilities won't use kiosks, or even if they do, they won't understand how to use them. This is wrong.

People with cognitive disabilities can and do use kiosks, just like everyone else. They might need extra time or help to complete a task, but with the right design, kiosks can be used by people with cognitive disabilities.

Unhelpful design is one of the main reasons people make this mistake. If the kiosk isn't designed properly, people with cognitive disabilities may find it difficult to use, so they simply don't bother. This means that the kiosk isn't accessible to them, even though it should be.

Another reason people make this mistake is because they fail to consider the specific needs of people with cognitive disabilities. They don't think about adding features like simplified instructions or extended time limits, which can make a huge difference to accessibility. They don't consider how the interface should be adjusted to make it easier to understand and use, or how visual and auditory cues could be used to help people with cognitive impairments.

People also forget to test their design with people with cognitive disabilities. This is vital in ensuring the design is effective and truly accessible. Feedback from people with cognitive disabilities can ensure that the design meets their needs.

Designing kiosks to be accessible to people with cognitive disabilities is essential. This means taking the time to consider the specific needs of users with cognitive disabilities, and making any necessary adjustments. Attention should also be given to features that make it easier to use the kiosk and to testing the design with people who may have cognitive disabilities. By making sure that kiosks are designed to be accessible to people with cognitive disabilities, we can make sure that everyone can benefit from them.

# 17. Designing for Multiple Languages

Designing for multiple languages can be a challenging task. In this chapter, we will explore the strategies for designing an interface that can be used by people from different linguistic backgrounds. We will discuss the importance of understanding the conventions of different languages, as well as the techniques that can be used to ensure the accessibility of a multilingual interface. We will also look at the challenges of supporting right-to-left languages, methods for retaining a user's language preference and effective ways to test the accessibility of a multilingual interface. This chapter will provide an invaluable resource for anyone involved in designing an interface for a global market.

◥ Why Designing for Multiple Languages Matters to You

In a small town in California, a team of kiosk designers were hard at work. They were designing a kiosk to help visitors access the local library. Each of the team members were passionate about their work and they wanted to make sure that the kiosk would be accessible to all.

The challenge they faced was that the local library catered to visitors speaking multiple languages. So, the team had to design a user interface that was intuitive and universal. They studied language conventions from around the world and worked tirelessly to create something that would work for everyone.

The team experienced a few setbacks and frustrations but eventually, with the help of their experience and expertise, they developed a kiosk that could be easily used in multiple languages. As the kiosk was unveiled, the team was filled with pride and joy. They witnessed visitors from all kinds of backgrounds using the kiosk with ease. This moment was a testament to the hard work, dedication, and passion of the entire design team. It was also a reminder that, with the right knowledge and effort, a universal design can be created and make life easier for people who need it the most.

❑ Understanding Languages in Different Markets

When designing a kiosk with accessibility in mind, it is important to consider the language usage in the target market. While English is a widely spoken language, there are many other languages used in different geographic locations around the world. Identifying the languages used in different markets is key to designing an accessible user interface.

First, you can get an overview of the languages used in different markets. Generally, a region will have more than one language associated with it. This means that you need to understand which language is the primary language of the country or region, as well as any other popular languages used in the area. Knowing the countries and

locations where these languages are spoken can help you determine which language to prioritize in your design.

Another key step is to analyze the popularity of languages over time and their corresponding growth. Language usage can change significantly over time, so it is important to be cognizant of any shifts in language popularity. This can help you determine which languages should be given priority when designing your kiosks. Additionally, you need to understand the distribution of different languages among the population. This will help you focus on the right language when designing a user interface that will be accessible for all users.

By understanding the languages used in different markets, you can more effectively design an accessible kiosk user interface. Thinking about the language needs of the target market can help you create a kiosk that is accessible to all users. This knowledge is key to making your kiosk design as inclusive as possible.

❑ Familiarizing with Different Language Conventions

When designing kiosks for an international market, familiarizing yourself with the conventions of different languages is essential. Each language has its own set of conventions that must be followed for a kiosk to be accessible to users fluent in that language.

When it comes to writing in a language, there may be different conventions to be aware of. For example, English is written in a left-to-right (LTR) format, while various languages like Arabic, Urdu, and Hebrew, are written in a right-to-left (RTL) format. It is important to recognize these differences when designing a kiosk interface and allow users to switch between their respective formats.

Certain languages also possess cultural nuances that are not found in others. In English, for instance, you may know that the punctuation mark "!" is used to express excitement. But in Japanese, a different punctuation mark is used for this purpose. If you are designing a kiosk for the Japanese market, you must understand these nuances in order to create an accessible interface.

Another factor to consider is proper grammar. A mistake in grammar can give a bad impression, so the kiosk user interface must be designed accurately for the language in question. This means understanding the rules of the language, such as verb tenses and pluralization, and making sure the kiosk reflects these rules. For example, a kiosk designed for a Spanish-speaking market should use verb conjugations and other linguistic features correctly.

Finally, there are various special terms or honorifics used in many languages that must be taken into account when designing a kiosk. In French, for instance, there are two forms of "you" that should be used depending on the context. If the kiosk is designed for use by the general public, the informal "tu" should be used when referring to the user. However, if the kiosk is designed for a professional context, the formal "vous" should be used instead.

By understanding the conventions of different languages, you can design a kiosk that accurately reflects the culture of the language in question. This will ensure the kiosk is accessible to users from all backgrounds and create a positive experience for everyone who uses it.

❑ Designing for Multiple Languages
Creating a user interface that caters to many different languages can be a complex and challenging task, but with the right combination of principles, tools, and strategies, it is possible to design a multilingual user interface that helps to engage users from all over the world.

The first step in creating a multilingual user interface is understanding the elements necessary for internationalization. This includes understanding the languages used in different markets and how popular each language is in different countries. It's also important to familiarize yourself with the conventions used in different languages, such as proper grammar, punctuation, and honorifics.

Once you have an understanding of the languages used in different markets, you can begin to design a user interface to accommodate multiple languages. There are a number of tools available to help in this process, such as plugins and frameworks, which can help make the process of multilingual user interface design much easier. Additionally, there are strategies you can use to display multiple languages within a menu or on buttons, such as 'unified text' and 'directional text'.

Once you have designed the user interface, it is important to make sure that it meets accessibility standards in all of the languages it supports. This involves adapting the user interface to accommodate language accessibility features, as well as testing the user interface for language accuracy and compatibility. Additionally, it's important to make sure that the user's language preference is retained in order to ensure a smooth experience for the user.

Finally, for languages that are written from right-to-left, such as Hebrew and Arabic, special adjustments to the user interface may be necessary. This involves adjusting the user interface to support right-to-left languages, as well as adapting graphics, navigation menus, and text to the language interface. Additionally, it's important to identify user language preferences accurately, as well as to test the interface for language accuracy and compatibility.

By following these steps, you can design a user interface that is accessible, user-friendly, and compatible with multiple languages. With the right combination of principles, tools, and strategies, you can create a multilingual user interface that helps to engage users from all over the world.

❑ Testing Accessibility for Different Languages

It's important to ensure your kiosk design is accessible for people of different languages. Many features of the kiosk, such as buttons, menus, and text, should be adjusted to fit the language of the user. This includes making sure the kiosk responds accurately to keystrokes, adjusting the fonts and layout to account for languages that read right-to-left, and accommodating language accessibility features.

When designing your kiosk, it's important to test for language translations to make sure there are no errors in context or words that don't translate properly. You should also test language features for compatibility with different web browsers. This ensures that the kiosk is accessible no matter what language the user is using, and no matter what type of device they are using to access the kiosk.

When it comes to accommodating language accessibility features, there are a few key elements to consider. For example, if the kiosk is voice activated, the language must be understood by the software. If the kiosk is text-based, it should accommodate keyboard entries for all languages. You should also consider the navigation between languages within the user interface. If a user can switch between languages, the interface must support that change seamlessly. Additionally, text should be displayed in the language of choice.

It's also important to retain a user's language preference. This can be done by determining the user's language preference, keeping track of the selected language in a database, and offering ways for the user to reset their language preference. It's important to be mindful of the cultural nuances of each language, such as proper grammar, punctuation and other formal or informal language conventions.

For right-to-left languages such as Arabic or Hebrew, it's important to adjust the user interface to accommodate these languages. This includes adapting graphics, navigation menus and text to the language interface. Additionally, you should identify user language preferences accurately, and test the interface for language accuracy and compatibility.

By testing the kiosk design for language accessibility, you can ensure that it is user-friendly and easily accessible for all users, no matter what language they are using. With careful design and consideration for language preferences, you can make sure that everyone has the opportunity to access your kiosk.

❑ Retaining a User's Language Preference
When designing an accessible kiosk, it is important to consider the language preferences of users. Keeping track of the language preferences of users is an important part of ensuring that your kiosks are accessible to all. This section will cover the principles of persistent language selection, the best practices for clearing and resetting language preferences, and how to keep track of selected language in a database.

❑ Determining User Language Preference
The first step to ensuring that your kiosks are language-friendly is to determine the most common language preferences of your users. If you are localizing your kiosks for a new area, it is essential to research the area to determine which language is the most popular. You should also consider looking at the language preferences of your current customers. By collecting this data, you can create a system to set the language of your kiosk to the most popular language in the local area.

❏ Principles of Persistent Language Selection

Once you have determined the language preferences of your users, it is important to ensure that the language preference is persistent. This means that once the user has selected the language of their preference, the kiosk should remember it for any future interactions. This will allow users to set the language once and not have to go through it each time they use the kiosk. To ensure this, the best practice is to store the language preference in a database and retrieve it whenever a user interacts with the kiosk.

❏ Best Practices for Clearing and Resetting Language Preferences

When users reset their language preferences, it is important to take that into consideration when designing your kiosk. This can be done by giving users the option to clear their language preferences and reset the kiosk to the default language. This ensures that if the user is no longer satisfied with the language of the kiosk, they can reset it and switch to a different language.

❏ Keeping Track of Selected Language in a Database

When storing language preferences in a database, it is important to keep track of the language selection so that the kiosk can read and recognize it. This can be done by creating separate fields in a database for each language preference. The language fields should be labeled in the language they correspond to and they should be able to support languages with different character sets. This will ensure that the kiosk can recognize, store, and retrieve the language preferences of your users.

❏ Conclusion

Designing accessible kiosks for multiple languages requires careful consideration of the language preferences of users. By researching the language preferences of the local area or collecting data from your current customers, you can determine the most popular language preferences of your users and set the language of your kiosk

accordingly. You should also consider creating a system to store the language preferences of users in a database, enabling the kiosk to remember the language settings for future use. Finally, it is important to give users the option to clear their language preference and reset the kiosk to the default language. With these tips, you will be able to design accessible kiosks that cater to the language preferences of all your users.

❑ Supporting Right-to-Left Languages

Designers of kiosks may come across situations where they need to accommodate right-to-left languages. For example, if they are creating a product that caters to an Arabic or Hebrew speaking market, they must design the user interface to support these languages. To do this, design teams should first familiarize themselves with the characteristics of right-to-left languages.

Generally speaking, these languages are written from right to left, rather than left to right like the majority of the world. This means that words, phrases and symbols appear in a different visual order in the interface compared to languages written left to right. Additionally, right-to-left languages can also contain characters that are written and read differently than those used in left-to-right languages.

To ensure the user interface is suitable for right-to-left languages, designers must adjust their basic elements and design principles. For example, a menu may have to be reversed, or the navigation arrows may have to switch from left to right. Furthermore, the language should be reversed and the text should be written from right to left.

Graphics, as well as text-based items, must be flipped or mirrored, as characters or symbols may be written differently when moving from left to right or vice versa. So, when designing for a right-to-left interface, it is important to remember to reverse or mirror any graphics or text-based items.

Designers must also pay attention to user language preferences. Identifying the user language correctly is key to providing users with an interface that is accommodating to their language. This can be done by using language detection plugins, however, it is also important to remember to keep track of the selected language and store it in a database. This can ensure that the user's language preferences are retained and are not lost when they log off.

Finally, designers should test the language interface thoroughly to ensure the accuracy of the text and the compatibility of the user interface with different web browsers. This will help ensure that the right-to-left language is presented correctly and that the user experience will be smooth and error-free.

By familiarizing themselves with the characteristics of right-to-left languages, adjusting the user interface for these languages, and testing for accuracy and compatibility, designers can create user interfaces that are accommodating and inclusive of people who use right-to-left languages. Doing so can help further promote accessibility and empower people with disabilities.

❑ Summary

This chapter laid out the importance of designing a user interface that can be easily accessed by a global audience. It identified the different languages in use in the market, showed the importance of familiarizing oneself with the conventions of each language, and illustrated how to best design a multilingual user interface. The chapter also discussed the importance of testing accessibility with different languages, retaining a user's language preference, and supporting right-to-left languages where necessary. By following these steps, a user interface can be designed to accommodate all global users.

◤ Examples of Effective Language Design Implementation

Person 1: Stella was tasked with designing a kiosk interface for a business in a multilingual city in Europe. She followed the advice given in this chapter, including making sure to familiarize herself with conventions of the various languages spoken in that city. Stella used this knowledge to create a user interface that made it easy for people to switch between their chosen language. She also tested accessibility with all the different languages, making any changes needed to ensure clear navigation and easy access for all users.

Person 2: Shani was setting up a kiosk in a museum in a Middle Eastern country with many different dialects. She read the advice in this chapter and understood the importance of language support. Shani wrote code that allowed users to choose their own language preference, and the interface would then use that language for the entire session. She also made sure to design the interface to support languages written from right-to-left, something she made sure to test thoroughly before launch.

Person 3: Lucy's job was to design an interactive kiosk for a retail store. She followed the advice in this chapter and made sure to design a multilingual user interface. She set up the interface to recognize a user's language preference and remember it for future visits. Lucy also tested the interface for any discrepancies between different translations and made any necessary changes. In the end, Lucy was able to create a kiosk that was accessible, regardless of language.

◼ Step-By-Step List of Effective Language Design Implementation Examples

1. Understand the different languages in use in the market – Research different languages spoken in the target market, record their frequencies.

2. Familiarize with conventions of different languages – Learn proper spelling and grammar rules and conventions of the languages used in the target market.

3. Consider multilingual user interface design – Utilize tools and techniques to create a seamless user experience for multiple languages.

4. Test accessibility with different languages – Test if users are able to access the interface and understand it when using various languages.

5. Retain a user's language preference – Store users' language preferences for future visits.

6. Support right-to-left languages where necessary – Design the user interface to accommodate right-to-left languages as necessary.

◼ Using a Framework to Design for Multiple Languages

The MAIN Framework:
Multilingual: Understand the different languages in use in the market.
Adaptability: Familiarize with conventions of different languages.
Interface: Consider multilingual user interface design.

Navigation: Test accessibility with different languages.

Preferences: Retain a user's language preference.

Order: Support right-to-left languages where necessary.

## ◣ Common Mistakes to Avoid When Designing for Multiple Languages

When designing kiosks, people often make the mistake of failing to consider different languages. This is a serious mistake, as a majority of the population speaks languages other than English. Without taking into account all the languages that could be used, your kiosk accessibility can be drastically reduced.

One of the main reasons why people overlook the importance of language is that it can be difficult for developers to understand different languages, cultures, and conventions. It can also be difficult to accommodate different language characters and input methods. While these are challenges to be aware of, they should not be used as an excuse to neglect the importance of taking language into account.

Another mistake people make is to overlook the importance of testing their interface with other languages. It is important to ensure that the user experience remains consistent across different languages. This includes everything from the size and design of text, to the navigation and menus. It is also important to make sure that the interface is compatible with right-to-left languages. Failure to do so can result in a poor user experience and can prevent users from accessing your kiosk.

Finally, it is important to allow users to retain their language preference throughout their user experience. This means that if a user switches to a different language, the interface should be able to follow suit. This helps users to navigate the kiosk easily and makes their experience more enjoyable.

In conclusion, it is important to be aware of the importance of language when designing kiosks. Developers should make sure that they consider different languages and cultures, test the interface across different languages, and retain user language preferences. Failing to do so can result in a poor user experience and can even prevent users from accessing the kiosk.

# 18. Adaption of Kiosks for Different Cultures

Designing an effective and inclusive kiosk involves taking into account cultural diversity, contexts and values which vary from one group of users to another. This chapter will explore the importance of understanding the cultural context of kiosk design, looking at the cultural values which shape user experience and researching user needs to meet the needs of different cultures. It will outline design guidelines for ensuring cultural acceptance of a kiosk and how to design user interfaces to suit different cultural preferences. We will also cover techniques to localise the kiosk design for different cultures. Make sure to read this chapter to gain valuable insights and learn how to create accessible and culturally accepted kiosks in a variety of contexts.

**◥ Understand Cultural Values to Design an Inclusive Kiosk - Learn How To Make A Difference.**

It was a sweltering summer day in a small village outside Chennai. In the center of town a woman named Lakshmi was struggling to use a kiosk designed to help her access medical care. The kiosk was not designed with accessibility in mind, and as a result it was too difficult for her to use. She tried for hours, but she could not get it to work.

Fortunately, help was on the way. A group of volunteers from the nearby city had heard about Lakshmi's plight and came to help. With their combined knowledge of the local culture, they were able to redesign the kiosk interface to make it more suited to the needs of the village. The team worked through the night, and the next day Lakshmi was able to use the kiosk with ease.

The story of Lakshmi is a powerful illustration of the importance of taking cultural considerations into account when designing kiosks. By understanding the needs of the local culture, the team of volunteers was able to create a kiosk that was truly accessible and could benefit many people in the village.

❑ Understanding Cultural Context

Designing a kiosk for accessibility isn't just about the technical details - it's also about understanding and accommodating cultural context. To do this, you need to understand what culture is, and what nuances exist between different cultural contexts.

Culture is a combination of shared beliefs, values, attitudes, and practices. It is unique to each group and affects how people in that group perceive the world, and how they interact with others. This means that people within a particular culture use different patterns of communication and interaction to get things done.

Kiosks, like any other kind of technology, are designed for a particular audience or culture. To ensure that your kiosk design is accessible to all, it's important to understand the cultural context of the users and their needs.

Careful research should be conducted to understand the values and beliefs that shape the user experience in a particular cultural context. This includes understanding the potential cultural meanings of colors and symbols, the nuances of language, and the user's abilities and needs.

Different cultural groups have different values and needs when it comes to technology. For example, a tactile interface may be more appropriate for people with limited vision, but it may not be accepted in certain cultural contexts. Similarly, icons or symbols that are meaningful in one culture might not be meaningful in another. Color meanings, font size preferences, and other aesthetic details may also differ on a cultural level.

Kiosk design should also take into account physical attributes such as size and weight, as these may differ among different cultural contexts. Additionally, cultural context should be taken into account when localizing content for different cultures.

Understanding and respecting cultural contexts is essential when designing kiosks for accessibility. By taking the time to research, understand, and accommodate cultural differences, you can create an inclusive user experience that respects and meets the needs of all users.

❏ Understanding Cultural Values in Kiosk Design

When designing kiosks with the intention of making them accessible to as many people as possible, it is important to understand the cultural values that may shape user experience. Different cultures around the world have different values, so it is important to be aware of these values in order to make sure that the kiosks are culturally acceptable and user-friendly.

❏ Identifying Relevant Cultural Values
When considering the cultural values that may influence design principles, one must consider values such as family, religion, and language. These, among other cultural values, may affect the way a kiosk should be designed. For example, a kiosk designed for a religious community may need to abide by certain guidelines that would not be applicable for another cultural context.

❏ Exploring Cultural Aspects that May Affect User Interface Design
Cultural values can also influence the choice of colors, symbols, and icons. Colors have different

connotations in different cultures, so it is important to consider this when designing the interface. Symbols and icons may also have different connotations, depending on the culture they are used in. For example, a symbol that is used in one culture as an indication of good luck may have a completely different meaning in another culture.

❑ Analyzing User Interface Design from a Cultural Perspective

In order to make sure that the user interface design is culturally appropriate and acceptable, it is important to understand the symbolic meanings of colors and symbols. This means taking into account the local culture, religious beliefs, and language in order to create a user-friendly and culturally appropriate interface. For example, a symbol that is widely accepted in one culture may have a completely different meaning in another, so it's important to pay attention to these nuances.

At the end of the day, understanding and appreciating the cultural values that shape user experience is key to designing accessible kiosks. By taking into account these cultural values, designers can create an interface that is user-friendly and culturally appropriate. This ensures that the kiosk is accepted among different cultures and makes life easier for those with disabilities.

❑ Researching User Needs to Accommodate Different Cultures

When designing a kiosk to suit the needs of people from a variety of cultures, it is important to research their needs. This research can provide vital insights into user preferences, allowing you to design a kiosk that best meets their needs.

The first step in researching the needs of different cultures is to identify your target audience, and the cultural context of these users. Depending on the intended audience, you may need to look at cultural factors such as religion, language, customs, and family values.

Once you understand the unique needs of your target audience, you can begin to understand their user experience. Understanding how different cultures interact with technology is essential to developing an effective kiosk design. What aspects of the design do users find difficult to use? Are there certain designs that are favoured or disliked? Are there any symbols or colours that need special consideration? Identifying potential issues in advance can help you to create a more user-friendly design.

Once you have established the user needs of your target audience, you can then begin to research user preferences. This research will help you to understand the specific needs of your target users, and tailor your kiosk design accordingly. Research techniques such as interviews and surveys can provide valuable insights into user preferences and behaviours. You can also use online research to learn about the needs of different cultures.

By researching the needs of different cultures, you can identify the elements that need to be included in your kiosk design. This research will also help you to understand how to construct the user interface to accommodate different cultures. From choice of colours and fonts, to icons and symbols – understanding the cultural context of your target users is essential for effective kiosk design.

Researching the needs of different cultures can provide invaluable insights into the development of an accessible and user-friendly kiosk. By gathering information about user preferences and cultures, you can create an effective designs that meets the needs of your target users. In addition, this research can also help you create designs that are culturally appropriate, ensuring that your kiosk design is accepted by the local population.

❏ Designing for Cultural Acceptance

Designing a user interface for a kiosk that is culturally acceptable can be a challenge. But understanding the cultural context of your user base and creating a user interface that is clear, concise and relevant to the culture can ensure a successful design.

The key elements to consider when designing a kiosk for cultural acceptance are colors, fonts, icons and other visual elements. When selecting colors for your design, consider the cultural context of the target audience and choose colors that are meaningful and appropriate to the culture. For example, the use of red in Chinese culture is associated with luck and prosperity, while in Western culture it is associated with danger and anger. Make sure to select colors that have positive connotations to the culture.

Fonts also play an important role in kiosk design when considering cultural acceptance. Select fonts that are easy to read and understandable in the context of the culture. Be aware that some languages may require specific fonts or localised versions of fonts. Additionally, remain mindful of the readability of the font and make sure that it is legible and easy to understand.

The use of visual elements such as icons, symbols and images can also help to create meaningful and culturally appropriate user interfaces. Select icons and symbols that are meaningful and appropriate to the culture. For example, if your kiosk is designed for a Western audience, an icon of a hand could mean 'help', but in a different culture, this icon might represent something entirely different. Similarly, be mindful of the use of images and choose ones that are meaningful and culturally appropriate.

Finally, it is important to ensure that your design is user-friendly and appropriate for the culture. To ensure a user-friendly design, make sure to keep the design clear, concise and easy to understand. Avoid using too many elements as this can make the design cluttered and confusing. Additionally, it is important to create a design that is culturally appropriate. Make sure that the design is relevant and meaningful to the user, taking into consideration the cultural context.

Designing a user interface for a kiosk that is culturally accepted can be a challenge. However, by understanding the culture and creating user interfaces that are clear, concise and culturally relevant, you can ensure a kiosk design that is both user-friendly and culturally accepted.

❑ Designing User Interfaces to Suit Different Cultural Preferences

When it comes to designing a kiosk, it is important to keep cultural context in mind. As the kiosk is going to be used by people from many different backgrounds, it is essential that the design is tailored to their needs.

The first step in designing user interfaces to suit different cultural preferences is to construct design elements that are appealing to different cultural groups. This means taking into account factors such as language, colours, symbols, and other visual cues. It is also important to consider physical characteristics such as size, shape, and weight. These factors should be taken into account to create a user interface that caters to different cultures.

Another element to consider when designing for different cultural preferences is the use of graphical elements. This can include the use of images, symbols, and icons, as well as different font sizes and typefaces. This can help to create a visual impact, increasing user engagement. Additionally, incorporating culturally relevant elements can add appeal to the user interface. This could include the use of meaningful symbols and colours, which have connotations in different cultures.

Finally, it is important to consider physical characteristics such as the size, shape, and weight of the kiosk. As kiosks are often placed in strategic locations, they need to be able to fit in with the surroundings. Depending on the culture and context of the kiosk, different physical designs may be more suitable than others.

By considering the different cultural preferences when designing user interfaces, kiosks can become more accessible and have a positive impact on the user experience. By creating a user-friendly and culturally appropriate interface, not only will the kiosks be more appealing to different cultural groups, but it can take one step closer to achieving an equitable society.

❏ Localizing Kiosk Design for Different Cultures

Designing a kiosk for different cultures requires an understanding of the cultural context of users. This includes taking into consideration values, preferences, and user needs that are specific to the target culture. Localizing a kiosk design involves carefully considering the visual elements, the language and the content so that it is both culturally relevant and user-friendly.

When localizing the content, it is important to think about the values associated with the culture. For instance, some cultures may have a preference for certain colors, symbols, and icons, whereas others may not. It is also important to consider how the user experience is affected by cultural context.

The next step is to conduct research to understand users' needs and preferences, taking into account cultural aspects. This can include things such as interviews, surveys, and focus groups. Understanding user needs is essential when designing a user interface that meets cultural expectations.

There are certain design guidelines that should be followed when creating an interface to meet cultural requirements. These include elements such as colors, fonts, and icons that should be chosen to appeal to the target culture. It is important to keep the design clear and concise, avoiding clutter that could confuse the user. Additionally, the design should be relevant and meaningful to the user, such as using culturally appropriate symbols and colors.

User interfaces should also be designed to be user-friendly and culturally appropriate. This includes elements such as the size and shape of the kiosk as well as its weight. The use of graphical elements can also help create a visual impact that is engaging for users.

Finally, technological innovations can be used to localize the design and user experience. This can include using language translation and text localization techniques. It is also important to understand the local market needs and preferences in order to create a kiosk that is culturally accepted.

By following the above advice, kiosk designs can be localized to meet the needs of different cultures. By understanding cultural values and conducting research to understand user preferences, it is possible to create a design that is both culturally relevant and user-friendly. By utilizing technology and considering elements such as colors, fonts, and icons, a design can be created that is likely to be accepted by the local culture.

❑ Conclusion

This chapter has explored the importance of understanding the cultural context of kiosk design, and the factors that contribute to the user experience. By researching user needs and taking into account cultural values, designers can ensure that their kiosks are accepted and utilised by users from different cultures. Design guidelines should be taken into consideration, such as the selection of colours, images and fonts, as well as addressing cultural preferences in user interfaces. Finally, adjusting the design to localise the kiosk for different cultures is an effective way of ensuring its success.

# ◥ Examples of Adapting Kiosks to Different Cultures - Learn How to Make a Difference.

1. Nicole is an app developer in a small rural town in the United States. She needed to design an app for her local community centre so that people with disabilities could get the same access everyone else had. She researched the needs of the different cultures in her area, as well as their language preferences and cultural values. She then incorporated this information into the design of her app. She used larger fonts and adapted the colors to be more pleasing to the local community. She also designed the app's navigation system to be intuitive and easy to use.

2. Tom is a designer in Hong Kong. He needed to create an interactive kiosk to be used in anti-discrimination campaigns in his city. He researched the needs of the different cultures in his city and designed a kiosk that incorporated symbols, colors and language preferences of the different cultures. He also included voice recognition and response options to help people with disabilities access the kiosk.

3. Susan is an architect in India. She needed to design a kiosk for use in public spaces. She studied the cultures, language and user needs in her area before she decided on the design of the kiosk. She tailored the user interface to make it easy to use for people from different cultures, incorporating symbols and colors from several cultures. She also added options for people who were visually impaired, like audio text-to-speech technology and raised buttons.

# ◥ Step by Step: Examples of Adapting Kiosks to Different Cultures

1. Importance of understanding cultural context for kiosk design
- Read up on recent studies on cultural context and kiosk design
- Analyse existing kiosks across different cultural settings
- Gather input from different stakeholders to understand cultural nuances and preferences

2. Understanding cultural values that shape the user Experience
- Research the cultural values of the target audience
- Find out how their values shape their user experience

- Identify how different cultural values impact the use of kiosks

3. Researching user needs to meet the needs of different cultures
- Conduct surveys and interviews with target audience
- Evaluate the user needs and preferences of different cultural groups
- Analyse the collected data to uncover insights

4. Design guidelines to ensure cultural acceptance of a kiosk
- Research and identify design principles for the targeted culture
- Develop and maintain design guidelines for the kiosk
- Integrate design guidelines into the development process

5. Designing user interfaces to suit different cultural preferences
- Identify and understand cultural preferences
- Design user interfaces to suit different cultural preferences
- Evaluate the design to ensure that it meets cultural standards

6. Techniques to localise the kiosk design for different cultures
- Research content and language preferences of the target culture
- Develop effective strategies to localize the kiosk design
- Test the localization strategies to ensure accuracy and appropriateness
- Make sure the design is culturally appropriate for the targeted culture.

◥ "Adapting Kiosks for Maximum Efficiency: A Step-by-Step Framework"

CULT - Cultural Understanding and Localisation of Technology:
1. Consider the cultural context of the kiosk.
2. Understand the values driving the user experience.
3. Research local user needs.
4. Create design guidelines for cultural acceptance.
5. Adapt the user interface to suit cultural preferences.
6. Localise the kiosk design.

◥ Common Mistakes to Avoid When Adapting Kiosks For Different Cultures

One of the most common mistakes that people make when designing kiosks for different cultures is failing to appreciate how much cultural context matters. A kiosk is a tool people interact with, and those interactions often involve cultural values, symbols and even language. People need to understand the cultural environment they are designing for in order to create successful kiosks.

Another common mistake is neglecting to research user needs in order to design kiosks that meet the needs of different cultures. It is essential to understand the culture and values of the intended user base before making any design decisions. This means talking to users and learning about their daily routines, preferences, and values. By understanding the cultural context, better-designed kiosks can be created.

A third mistake people make is failing to design around the cultural values and preferences of different cultures. Just as people from different countries speak different languages, so too do people from different cultures have different expectations when it comes to interacting with technology. For example, some cultures find it difficult to use touchscreens, while others are more comfortable with them. It is important to consider cultural values and preferences when designing kiosks.

Finally, another mistake is that people often forget to localise the kiosk design for different cultures. Localisation involves customizing the kiosk interface to fit the language and cultural preferences of the intended users. This includes everything from changing the language settings, to designing icons and colours that are culturally appropriate. Doing this makes it much easier for users to use the kiosk, as they will a see design that is familiar and easy to understand.

Making any one of these mistakes can lead to kiosks that aren't usable for people from different cultures, so it is important for designers to understand the importance of cultural context when designing kiosks. By considering user needs, designing around cultural values and preferences, and localising the kiosk design, designers can ensure that their kiosks are accessible and usable for people from all different cultures.

# 19. Ensuring Compliance with Disability Laws

This chapter explores the importance of ensuring compliance with disability laws when designing kiosks and interfaces. It outlines the scope of disability laws while helping to develop an understanding of reasonable accommodations. Additionally, it provides a plan for ensuring compliance with any applicable disability laws, highlights the resources necessary to achieve compliance and explains how to create systems for adjusting kiosks and interfaces for users with disabilities. Finally, it evaluates the impact of any changes made for users with disabilities. Let's take a look at the steps necessary to ensure accessible kiosks for all users.

Tina had a dream. She wanted to make the world more accessible to those with disabilities, so that everyone could have the same rights and opportunities. But she knew it would be a struggle. She worked in a small town in the United States and had limited access to resources and technology. With only a few months to meet a deadline, Tina was determined. She started researching the laws that protect disabled citizens and the resources necessary to ensure compliance. Every night she devoted her time to assessing the existing kiosks and developing an understanding of what adjustments would need to be made to make them accessible. After long days and sleepless nights, Tina was able to provide kiosks that were compliant with the existing disability laws and provided an improved user experience for those with disabilities. Her passion and dedication had made a big difference in her community and helped make the world more accessible for everyone.

## # Understanding the Scope of Existing Disability Laws

Disability laws exist to ensure that people with disabilities have the same rights to access and use products, services, and environments as those without disabilities. Kiosk design is no exception. When designing kiosks, it is important to understand the scope of disability laws and to make sure that the design of the kiosk complies with all relevant laws and regulations.

The term "disability law" is used to refer to state and federal laws that protect the rights of people with disabilities. These include laws such as the Americans with Disabilities Act (ADA) and Section 504 of the Rehabilitation Act. In addition, many states and local jurisdictions have their own laws and regulations that protect the rights of people with disabilities. It is important to understand both the federal and the state and local laws when designing kiosks.

Kiosk design must comply with all legal requirements in order to ensure that people with disabilities can use the kiosk. This includes making sure that the kiosk is ADA compliant, which means that it must be accessible to people with a wide range of disabilities. This includes making sure that it is easy to use, has accessible features such as accessible keyboards, and is designed with universal design principles in mind.

In addition to understanding the scope of existing disability laws, it is also important to understand the rights and responsibilities of all stakeholders. This includes understanding the rights of the user, such as the right to access information and the right to access products and services. It also includes understanding the responsibilities of the kiosk designer, such as the duty to provide access to the kiosk and to ensure that it is designed according to all applicable laws and regulations.

Finally, when designing kiosks, it is important to review any local laws or ordinances that may be relevant. These laws and ordinances may have additional requirements for kiosk design that go beyond the scope of the federal and state laws. For example, a local ordinance may require that all kiosks be wheelchair accessible.

By understanding the scope of existing disability laws, reviewing the rights and responsibilities of all stakeholders, and reviewing any local laws or ordinances, designers can ensure that the kiosk design is compliant with all applicable laws and regulations. This is crucial for ensuring that people with disabilities have equal access to kiosks, and for creating products and services that are accessible to everyone.

❑ Developing an Understanding of Reasonable Accommodations

Reasonable accommodations are important when designing kiosks for people with disabilities. These are adjustments that are made to make a space more accessible for those with disabilities. This is done in order to ensure that all users, regardless of their ability level, have access to technological resources, such as the kiosks.

When it comes to reasonable accommodations, the key is understanding the potential benefits of making them. These benefits include increased safety, increased convenience, increased accessibility, and improved user experience. Reasonable accommodations also provide a sense of security and respect for those with disabilities.

In order to prepare reasonable accommodations, you must first establish criteria for them. This includes understanding the legal requirements for compliance, identifying strategies for achieving compliance, and defining the roles and responsibilities of all stakeholders. Additionally, it is important to establish a timeline for implementing reasonable accommodations and to measure the impact of any changes.

It is also important to understand the duty of care to all users when it comes to reasonable accommodations. This means ensuring that all users have access to the same information and experiences, regardless of their disability. This ensures that all users have the same level of comfort and convenience, as well as a sense of respect and dignity.

Finally, when it comes to reasonable accommodations, it is important to set a timeline for implementing them. This will ensure that the necessary changes are made promptly and that all users have access to the same quality of service. Additionally, this timeline should include a review process in order to ensure that all reasonable accommodations are implemented correctly.

These are just a few tips for developing an understanding of reasonable accommodations when designing kiosks for people with disabilities. With this knowledge, you can create an accessible and user-friendly environment for all users.

❑ Creating a Plan to Ensure Compliance with Disability Laws

When it comes to making kiosks and other technology accessible to all people, including those with disabilities, compliance with disability laws is essential. This section will provide an overview of the legal requirements for compliance, strategies for achieving compliance, and resources for ensuring that kiosks are fully accessible.

❑ Understanding the Legal Requirements for Compliance

Before creating a plan for compliance, it is necessary to understand the legal requirements for kiosk design. Different countries and regions will have different laws and regulations, so it is important to research the specific laws applicable to your area. Generally speaking, the legal requirements will relate to the rights of disabled people, including the right to equal access to technology, services, and public spaces. It is important to be aware of the local laws, as well as any federal laws that might apply in your area.

❑ Identifying Strategies for Achieving Compliance

Once you have an understanding of the legal requirements, you can begin to develop strategies for achieving compliance. Depending on the particular disability laws in your area, you may need to adjust the design of your kiosks, provide additional training for staff, or create reasonable accommodations for disabled users. It is important to consider all of these possibilities when creating a plan.

❑ Defining the Roles and Responsibilities of Different Stakeholders

Achieving compliance with disability laws requires the collaboration of all stakeholders, including the kiosk manufacturer, the customer, and the user. It is important to clearly outline the roles and responsibilities of each stakeholder. For example, the kiosk manufacturer may be responsible for the design and implementation of the kiosks, the customer may be responsible for providing reasonable accommodations, and the user may be responsible for reporting any issues with accessibility.

❑ Creating a Timeline for Achieving Compliance

Once the roles and responsibilities of each stakeholder are established, it is important to create a timeline for achieving compliance with disability laws. This timeline should include milestones for purchasing equipment, making necessary adjustments, providing training, and making other necessary changes. It is important to set realistic deadlines and make sure that everyone is on the same page with regards to the timeline.

❑ Measuring the Impact of Any Changes

Ultimately, the goal of complying with disability laws is to ensure that all users have equal access to technology, services, and public spaces. It is important to measure the impact of any changes that you make to ensure that they are having a positive effect. This can include collecting feedback from users, conducting usability tests, and measuring the performance of the kiosk over time.

By following these steps, you will be able to create a plan to ensure compliance with disability laws. Not only will this help you to create a better user experience, but it will also ensure that you are in compliance with the law. Ultimately, this will help to make the future more accessible for everyone.

❑ Determining the Resources Necessary to Achieve Disability Law Compliance
When designing your kiosk, it's essential to consider the resources needed to ensure that it meets all applicable disability laws. This section will cover the steps you should take to determine the resources necessary for achieving compliance.

❑ Estimating the Cost of Achieving Compliance
The first step in determining the resources necessary for compliance is to estimate the cost. This can be done by considering the total cost of materials, labor and any additional services such as programming or testing. Make sure that all of these costs are taken into account when making this estimation.

❑ Prioritizing Resources and Time to Achieve Compliance Quickly
Once the cost of achieving compliance has been estimated, it's important to prioritize resources and time in order to reach compliance as quickly as possible. This can be done by focusing on the most important changes that need to be made first, and then ensuring that these are addressed within the allotted timeframe.

❑ Identifying and Hiring Additional Resources (If Needed)
In some cases, it may be necessary to identify and hire additional resources in order to achieve compliance. This could include hiring additional developers, designers or testers, or engaging a consultant to provide advice and guidance. It's important to consider the time and cost implications of hiring additional resources when estimating the cost of compliance.

❑ Establishing a Budget for Achieving Compliance

Once the cost of achieving compliance has been estimated, it's important to set a sensible budget so that plans are realistic and manageable. Make sure to consider any potential savings or cost reductions that may be achievable too.

❑ Reviewing the Need for Additional Resources

Finally, it's important to review the need for any additional resources that may be necessary to achieve compliance. This could include specialised testing tools, assistive technologies or software, and any training that may be required. Consider the cost of all these resources and factor them into the overall cost of compliance.

By estimating the cost of achieving compliance, prioritizing resources and time, identifying and hiring additional resources (if needed), establishing a budget and reviewing the need for additional resources, you can develop a strategy for ensuring that your kiosk meets all the applicable disability laws. With the right plan in place, you can ensure that your kiosk is accessible and user-friendly for all of your users.

❑ Creating Systems for Adjusting Kiosks and Interfaces for Users with Disabilities

When designing a kiosk for people with disabilities, it's essential to consider how the system can be adjusted for their needs. Knowing the extent of any modifications that may be needed and designing adjustable interfaces can help ensure that everyone can take full advantage of the kiosk and its features.

The first step in creating a system for adjusting kiosks and interfaces is to identify the need for modification. In some cases, it may be obvious that a user with a disability needs a special adjustment to use the kiosk, but it's important to consider the individual's individual needs. This could involve an assessment of the user's disability and any special adaptations that may be needed.

Once the need for modification is identified, it's important to estimate the extent of any modification needed. This could involve a review of existing equipment, possible alternative technologies, and any necessary changes to the user interface to make it more accessible. It's also important to consider any special training and resources that may be needed to help users adjust to the system.

After the need for modification is identified and estimated, the next step is to design adjustable interfaces. This could involve creating a more user-friendly and intuitive system, adjusting the interface to accommodate wheelchair users, or making other changes to make the system more accessible. It's important to consider any special requirements for the user, such as the ability to see and reach all controls, or the need for an alternative input device.

In addition to designing adjustable interfaces, it's also important to establish the need for additional training. This could involve providing step-by-step instructions, creating tutorials, or providing special training sessions to help users adapt to the system. It's also important to consider the time and resources necessary for providing the additional training.

Finally, it's important to review the need for additional assistive technology. This could involve making sure the system is compatible with any special devices, such as screen readers or voice input, or ensuring that the system can accommodate alternative methods of navigating the interface. It's also important to consider any special needs, such as braille output or tactile feedback.

Creating systems for adjusting kiosks and interfaces for users with disabilities is an important step in making sure that everyone can use the kiosk. Identifying the need for modification, estimating the extent of any modification needed, designing adjustable interfaces, establishing the need for additional training, and reviewing the need for additional assistive technology can help ensure that your kiosk is as accessible and user-friendly as possible.

❏ Analyzing the Impact of Changes on Kiosk Users

When making changes to a kiosk to ensure compliance with disability laws, it is important to evaluate the impact on users. It is essential to measure the degree of impact, determine the system's usability after implementation, and develop strategies for monitoring performance. In addition, finding ways to improve user experience is key to creating an accessible system.

When assessing the impact of any changes, consider the implications for both disabled and non-disabled users. For example, increasing the text size or changing the keyboard layout could benefit users with visual impairments, while also making the system more accessible for users with cognitive disabilities. However, such changes may also affect the speed of the system, or introduce features that are difficult to use for physically impaired users.

It is also important to measure the degree of impact on users. This can be done by tracking performance before and after the changes have been implemented. Evaluating the usability of the system after implementation should also be part of the process. This can be done by observing users' experiences, collecting feedback from users, and using metrics to measure usage.

Developing strategies for monitoring performance is also key. This can be done by setting up metrics to track key performance indicators and monitoring user feedback. These strategies are necessary to ensure that changes are meeting the needs of users and to ensure compliance with disability laws.

Finally, finding ways to improve the user experience is essential. This could include making adjustments to the interface, such as increasing the contrast of the text or making the text easier to read. Adjustments to the user input mechanisms, such as providing alternative input devices, can also be beneficial. Additionally, training users on how to use the system can improve their experience.

By carefully assessing the impact of any changes on users, it is possible to ensure compliance with disability laws, while optimizing the usability of the system for all users. By monitoring the performance of the system, finding ways to improve user experience, and ensuring that adjustments are meeting the needs of users, it is possible to design an accessible and user-friendly system.

❑ Conclusion

This chapter covered the importance of understanding and adhering to disability laws. The main topics discussed included understanding the scope of existing disability laws, developing an understanding of reasonable accommodations, creating a plan to ensure compliance with any disability laws, determining the resources necessary to achieve disability law compliance, creating systems for adjusting kiosks and interfaces for users with disabilities, and analyzing the impact of any changes on users of the kiosk. A thorough understanding of disability laws and a plan to ensure compliance is an essential element of successful business operations.

## ◼ Examples of Implementing Disability Laws in Everyday Life

Person 1: Maria owns a small cafe and wanted to ensure her store was compliant with disability laws. She took the advice from this chapter and created a plan for her store that included making sure all of her staff had training for interacting with customers with disabilities. She also reviewed the aisles of her store and adjusted the layout to make sure it was accessible for wheelchairs.

Person 2: Nick runs a local bank and he used the advice from this chapter to review his bank's kiosk interfaces. He determined the resources necessary to add features that allowed customers with disabilities to use the kiosk with ease. He implemented different voice recognition systems and Braille keyboards to give customers with impairments more control over their transactions.

Person 3: Helen is the manager of her city's transportation system. She used the advice from this chapter to analyze the impact of any changes they made to the kiosks. She looked at the various features they had and identified ways to help people with disabilities use the kiosks more easily. She also implemented systems for adjusting the kiosks to make them more accessible to people with impairments.

## ◼ Step by Step: Examples of Implementing Disability Laws in Everyday Life

Stage 1: Understanding the Scope of Existing Disability Laws
- Research and familiarize yourself with local and federal disability laws
- Gather detailed records of what compliance with these laws require

Stage 2: Developing an Understanding of Reasonable Accommodations
- Learn what types of reasonable accommodations can be used to help make the kiosk accessible

- Research the different standards and regulations in your area regarding reasonable accommodations

Stage 3: Creating a Plan to Ensure Compliance with Any Disability Laws
- Assess if and how existing designs can be modified to meet legal requirements
- Develop a plan for making alterations or creating new products or features to meet legal requirements

Stage 4: Determining the Resources Necessary to Achieve Disability Law Compliance
- Estimate the costs associated with making any changes to existing designs or creating new products or features
- Identify the personnel, tools, and materials needed for the project

Stage 5: Creating Systems for Adjusting Kiosks and Interfaces for Users With Disabilities
- Create an easy-to-follow process for making changes to the kiosk to accommodate users with disabilities
- Develop a system for tracking the changes made and ensuring they are properly implemented

Stage 6: Analyzing the Impact of Any Changes on Users of the Kiosk
- Survey existing users and determine their level of satisfaction with the kiosk's current accessibility
- Monitor user feedback to determine how any changes to the kiosk affect the user experience

## ◥ A Practical Framework for Ensuring Compliance with Disability Laws

The ABCD Compliance Framework:
A - Analyze the impact of any changes on users of the kiosk
B - Develop an understanding of reasonable accommodations
C - Create systems for adjusting kiosks and interfaces for users with disabilities
D - Determine the resources necessary to achieve disability law compliance.

❑ Common Mistakes to Avoid When Designing Accessible Kiosks

One of the most common mistakes people make when designing kiosks that are accessible to people with disabilities is not considering the user experience. People may think they are designing a kiosk that is usable by someone with a disability, but they often overlook important issues such as ease of navigation, minimal user input, and font size. For example, if the font size used on a kiosk is too small, it can be difficult for some people with vision impairments to read the text. Additionally, if the navigation of the kiosk isn't clear or intuitive, it can be confusing and frustrating for users.

Another mistake people make when designing kiosks is not accounting for the different types of disabilities a user might have. People with disabilities are not a monolith; different users will have different needs and preferences when it comes to interacting with a kiosk. For example, someone who is deaf might need captions on a video or a way to communicate with the kiosk through a text-based interface. Someone with a mobility impairment might need a kiosk that is wheelchair-accessible or has voice-controlled options. It's important to consider the different needs of users when designing an accessible kiosk so that everyone is able to benefit from its use.

Lastly, people often overlook the importance of testing their kiosk design thoroughly. It is essential to make sure that the kiosk works for all users, regardless of their disability. This means testing for a range of disabilities, using assistive technologies, and considering both the technical and the human-centered interface. By testing the kiosk design thoroughly, it's possible to identify any potential problems before they become a problem for the user.

Overall, designing a kiosk that is accessible for people with disabilities is an important and complex task. It's important to consider the user's experience, account for different types of disabilities, and make sure the kiosk design is tested thoroughly. By following these steps, it's possible to create a kiosk that can empower people with disabilities.

## 20. Conclusion: Making the Future Accessible for Everyone

Welcome to the Conclusion of Making the Future Accessible for Everyone. This chapter will provide guidance and strategies for ensuring your kiosk designs are universally accessible, regardless of age, ability, culture, or language. We will discuss how to account for different disabilities when designing a kiosk, how to adhere to disability laws, and how to develop keyboard layouts that are accessible for all users. Additionally, we will look into the various testing strategies that can be used to make sure your kiosk design meets accessibility standards. By the end of this chapter, you will have the knowledge and confidence to create an inclusive and accessible design for your kiosks.

◗ Unlocking Accessibility for All - Why This Chapter is Essential for Making Kiosk Designs Inclusive.

It was a blistering hot day in the industrial port of Lüderitz, Namibia. Anne had been born with cerebral palsy, a condition that affects her mobility, making it difficult for her to use her hands. Despite her physical disability, Anne had always been determined to lead an independent life.

Anne had been offered a job at a local fishing company, but knew she wouldn't be able to perform the tasks without the right tools. That's when she realised that the kiosk installed in the office was simply not accessible to her.

She went to her supervisor and asked for help. Anne was told that universal design was an expensive and complicated affair for a small business like theirs, so she decided to take matters into her own hands. With the help of a few kind-hearted colleagues, Anne made several adjustments to the kiosk interface, making it more accessible for her to use.

It was a long journey, but eventually Anne was able to do the job she had been hired for. From then on, Anne was an example to others of the importance of universal design, and her story spread across the fishing industry, inspiring other small companies to pay more attention to accessibility.

❑ Making the Future Accessible for Everyone

Universal design is a key factor to ensuring kiosks are accessible to people with disabilities, and can make life easier for everyone. Universal design is based on creating products, content and services that can be used by all people regardless of their age, ability, or situation. This approach can help to create a more inclusive environment, and offers both social and economic benefits.

Some of the main features of universal design include features like braille keypads, voice commands and more. These features should be easy to use and understand, and provide the user with an enjoyable and accessible experience. Other principles of universal design include flexibility, usability and visualization.

In addition to understanding universal design, it is also important to be aware of the various disabilities that can affect accessibility. Different disabilities often require different measures and considerations when it comes to kiosk design, from physical impairments to cognitive disabilities and more. These challenges must be taken into account when designing for usability and accessibility.

Adhering to legal guidelines, such as the Americans with Disabilities Act (ADA), is also essential when designing for accessibility. Making sure your design complies with these laws will help to avoid potential legal risks and ensure the rights of disabled people are respected.

It is also important to consider the various cultural aspects when designing for different cultures. Every culture is unique and its own set of values, customs and language. As a result, it is important to understand how culture can affect accessibility and to make sure that accessibility is an integral part of the design process. This can include things such as adding language options, creating more appropriate colour palettes, making fonts more readable, and more.

Finally, having an accessible keyboard layout can also make a big difference. The layout should be ergonomic and provide tactile feedback, as well as having text size and clarity options that are appropriate for the user. Braille keypads are examples of designs that use ergonomics and tactile feedback to make them accessible to people with disabilities.

Testing is a key part of ensuring that the design meets accessibility standards. Using a combination of heuristic testing, focus groups, surveys, A/B testing, and other methods can help to ensure that the design is as accessible as possible. Tools like screen readers can be used to measure the performance of the kiosk, offering valuable insights into how it can be improved for accessibility.

Universal design, knowledge of different disabilities, compliance with relevant laws and cultural considerations are all essential aspects of making the future accessible for everyone. Designing accessible kiosks is an important way to empower those with disabilities and create an environment where everyone has equal access.

❏  Designing for Different Disabilities

Designing kiosks to suit people with disabilities can seem like a daunting task, but with the right approach, it doesn't have to be. It is important to understand the types of disabilities and the challenges that come with designing for each one. For example, designing for those with physical disabilities will likely require implementing technologies such as alternative inputs, while designing for those with cognitive disabilities may require creating user-friendly layouts and font sizes. There are also accessibility guidelines that need to be taken into account depending on the region that the kiosk will be operating in, as well as cultural considerations.

When designing for people with physical disabilities, certain features can help make access easier. An ergonomic and tactile keyboard is a must, providing users a physical means of input. Voice control can also be used, enabling those with limited mobility to navigate using vocal commands. Alternative input methods such as switch access, touchpads and eye-tracking can also make things easier. Performing usability testing with people who have physical disabilities is essential, as this allows you to make sure that your design is both accessible and user-friendly.

Designing for people with cognitive disabilities also requires careful consideration. User-friendly layouts and font sizes are key, as well as the inclusion of features such as audio support or colour-coded text for people with Dyslexia. It is also important to make sure that your kiosk is designed in a way that it is easy to navigate, as those with cognitive disabilities may need additional time and guidance to get around. Finally, considering accessibility options for people with cognitive impairments is paramount.

Designing for people with visual impairments is perhaps the most challenging as there is a need to consider both the hardware and the software. Accessible colour palettes and font sizes are key, as well as the use of high contrast elements. Audio cues and textual descriptions of images can also help those with visual impairments interact with the kiosk. Additionally, it is important to consider alternative input methods, as those with visual impairments may not be able to interact with the traditional keyboard and mouse inputs.

Designing for those with hearing impairments is also an important consideration. Accessible visual cues are essential, such as images and written instructions. Providing informative audio messages that are clear and concise is also important, as is ensuring that volume and tone levels are adjustable. The inclusion of closed captioning or sign language translation can also be beneficial.

It is clear that designing kiosks for people with disabilities requires careful consideration in order to ensure that the design meets accessibility standards. From understanding the principles of universal design to developing strategies for testing, this chapter has provided an overview of the steps required in order to create an accessible kiosk. By following these steps, it is possible to create a kiosk design that is both accessible and user-friendly, empowering those with disabilities to access the services they need.

❑  Making the Future Accessible for Everyone

Creating accessible kiosks is no small feat. With so many aspects to consider, it is essential to understand the laws surrounding disability rights and universal design. These are legal frameworks that protect the rights of people with disabilities and ensure their fair and equal treatment.

The Americans with Disabilities Act (ADA) is the most commonly referred law in the US. This law stipulates that any public spaces must be designed to be accessible for people with disabilities. It does this through the implementation of universal design principles. This means that any public place must be designed in a way that can be used be all people, regardless of physical, mental, or sensory ability.

Section 504 of the Rehabilitation Act of 1973 is another federal law that deals specifically with accessibility in public spaces. It prohibits discrimination on the basis of disability and also requires that reasonable accommodations are made for people with disabilities. Other laws such as the Respect for Disabled Persons' Rights law in Japan also provide similar guidance and protection.

The implications of these laws on kiosk design is significant. Any kiosk design must meet the standards of these laws in order to be legally compliant. This means that their design must incorporate elements that are accessible to all people, thus validating all areas of the kiosk. Additionally, accommodations must be made in layout and design, such as providing options for users to enter required information with alternative forms of input, such as voice or Braille.

Failing to comply with these laws can have serious legal implications. This can include civil or criminal penalties, depending on the severity of the case. In addition to legal action, companies may also face financial consequences from not upholding the law, such as reparations and damages.

Ultimately, ensuring universal design and compliance with disability laws should be at the forefront of any kiosk design. This is the only way to ensure that all people have access to the service or product provided and can be assured of their rights. By understanding and respecting these laws, designers can work towards creating a better future for everyone.

❑ Making Kiosks Accessible to Different Cultures

When designing kiosks and other forms of technology, it is important to ensure that all cultures are adequately represented and accessible. Different cultures have unique audio, visual, and language preferences that must be taken into consideration when building accessible kiosks.

Language can be a key factor in how people interact with kiosk technology. If a kiosk is designed for an audience with limited English proficiency, it is important to attempt to localize it in the language of the target audience. This can be done by adding languages with the correct alphabet and language syntax, as well as including cultural icons in the interface. Additionally, text should be written in a large, legible font to ensure it is accessible for all.

The colour palette of the kiosk also needs to be taken into account when designing for different cultures. Generally, it is important to maintain a consistent colour palette throughout the interface. However, some cultures may have colour associations that should be taken into account when developing the interface. Additionally, it's important to ensure the contrast is high enough for colourblind people to be able to use the kiosk.

The layout of the kiosk is also important when designing for different cultures. This includes both the physical layout of the kiosk as well as the order of the user interface. In order to make the kiosk more accessible, it is important to include universal design principles such as flexibility, usability, and visualization. For example, it is helpful to include an adjustable table to ensure the kiosk can be used by those of all heights and sizes. Additionally, the order of the interface should be designed to be intuitive and easy to understand.

The keypad of the kiosk should also be designed to be accessible for all cultures. For example, if the kiosk is designed for users with limited English proficiency, the keypad should include a layout that matches the language's alphabet and syntax. Additionally, Braille keypads can also be used for users who are visually impaired.

Ultimately, when designing kiosks with accessibility in mind, it is important to consider the needs of all cultures. This can be done by providing language options, using appropriate colour palettes, incorporating universal design principles, and using accessible keypads. By doing so, kiosk technology can be made accessible to everyone.

❏ Understanding Accessible Keyboard Layouts

When designing tech for people with disabilities, accessibility is a key factor. A fundamental part of an accessible design are the keyboards used – this includes both virtual and physical keyboards. An accessible keyboard is one which is designed to be used without difficulties by users with physical, cognitive and visual impairments. To make a keyboard accessible, it should include ergonomic design, tactile feedback and other features which are easy to use and understand.

One of the main considerations when designing an accessible keyboard is the layout. The standard keyboard layout is known as 'QWERTY' and is most commonly used across the world. Other keyboard layouts such as Dvorak and AZERTY have been developed to improve typing speed, accuracy and comfort. They can also be used to design an accessible keyboard for users with disabilities.

When choosing an accessible keyboard layout, it is important to consider the text size and clarity, colour contrast and other features of the design. For users with vision impairments, larger font sizes, high contrast and clear labels can help them more easily interact with the design. Additionally, tactile feedback can be incorporated into the design for those with physical impairments. This feedback can be in the form of a Braille keypad or raised bumps which indicate the keys on a physical keyboard.

It is also important to consider ergonomic layouts which allow users to type comfortably. An example of this is the 'split' layout which places the keys along the edges of the keyboard. This allows users to type with their arms, elbows and wrists in a more natural posture.

Finally, it is important to test the design to ensure it meets the needs of users with disabilities. Testing is the process of evaluating the design to ensure it is accessible and usable by all. This includes focus groups, surveys, A/B testing and other techniques to measure the design against accepted standards. This can include the AbilityNet accessibility guidelines or the Web Content Accessibility Guidelines (WCAG).

When designing accessible keyboards, it is important to take into account the needs of people with disabilities. This includes considering different keyboard layouts, visual and tactile feedback, ergonomic layouts and testing the design to ensure it meets accessibility standards. By taking these considerations into account and designing an accessible keyboard, you can create a user-friendly interface which is comfortable and convenient for all.

Testing kiosk design to ensure it meets accessibility standards is an important part of creating kiosks that are accessible for people with disabilities. Without proper testing, a kiosk may be difficult or impossible for certain people to use. However, with the right kind of testing, you can ensure that your design meets accessibility standards and that your kiosk is accessible for everyone.

There are several processes you can use to test your design. Heuristic testing and focus groups are two popular methods. Heuristic testing uses experts to examine the design for potential problems and suggest ways to make it more accessible. Focus groups involve having people with disabilities provide feedback on the design to identify any potential difficulties with using it. Both of these approaches can be helpful in finding areas where the design may not meet accessibility standards.

It's also important to familiarize yourself with the guidelines and standards used to determine accessibility. AbilityNet and the Web Content Accessibility Guidelines (WCAG) are two guidelines that you should follow when testing your design. AbilityNet provides guidance on how to design for people with different disabilities, while WCAG specifies minimum requirements for making online content accessible.

When testing your design, it's important to consider how different kinds of people will interact with it. For example, you should use accessibility testing tools like screen readers to make sure your design is readable for people with visual impairments, and you should also consider the alternative inputs available for different disabilities.

Finally, it's important to make sure your design takes into account different cultures and languages. When designing for different cultures, you should consider the language options available, font sizes, colour palettes and different keyboard layouts.

By following the processes mentioned above, you can make sure your kiosk meets accessibility standards and is accessible for everyone. Testing your design with the right guidelines, tools and sensitivity to different cultures will ensure that your kiosk is inclusive for all users.

❑ Sub-heading: Finding the Future Accessible for All

This chapter looked into the importance of universal design and the various challenges of designing for different disabilities. It explored the impact of disability laws, different keyboard layouts and the need to take into account cultures. Strategies for testing were also provided to ensure the design meets accessibility standards. With all these considerations in mind, we can make the future accessible for everyone.

◥ Inclusive Design In Action: Putting Accessibility Into Practice

1. John is a kiosk designer who works with people with vision impairments. He implemented a keyboard layout which was easier to navigate with a Braille reader. He also added audio cues so that users could hear the names of the buttons they needed to press. He tested his design multiple times with different users to make sure it was accessible.

2. Melanie is a kiosk designer who works with people with motor impairments. She included buttons which were large enough to be easily pressed by people with limited mobility. She also included multiple adjustable settings that could be tailored to different users' needs. She tested her design multiple times with different users to make sure it was accessible.

3. Andrew is a kiosk designer who works with people from different cultural backgrounds. He designed a kiosk which could be used in multiple languages. He also created a simple design that would be understood by all cultures. He tested his design multiple times with different users to make sure it was accessible.

◤ Step-By-Step Guide: Putting Accessibility Into Practice

Understand the importance of Universal Design:
- Research the principles of Universal Design
- Take time to understand the needs of your target groups
- Think through how to design a kiosk that works for all users

Be aware of the various challenges of designing for different disabilities:
- Research different impairments and their needs
- Look into how design needs to change based on different disabilities
- Learn what features would make your kiosk more accessible

Know the impact of disability laws:
- Research the different legislations and regulations
- Understand how laws from different countries can affect your design
- Check if your design meets the accessibility standards

Explore how different cultures may need to be taken into account:
- Research the main cultural differences
- Research if certain cultural norms must be taken into consideration
- Think about how to design a kiosk that works for all cultures

Look into different keyboard layouts that are accessible:
- Research different keyboard layouts
- Identify which keyboard layouts are the most accessible
- Evaluate how to set up the most accessible keyboard layout

Develop strategies for testing to ensure the design meets accessibility standards:

- Research different testing strategies

- Test the design with different users to check if it is accessible

- Evaluate the results and make amendments if necessary


◥ Introducing a Practical Framework for Accessibility


GIGADA:

G - Get to grips with Universal Design

I - Identify Challenges Based On Different Disabilities

G - Go Through Disability Laws

A - Account For Cultural Requirements

D - Design With Accessible Keyboard Layouts

A - Assess With Testing That Meets Accessibility Standards


◥ Common Mistakes to Avoid When Developing Accessible Kiosks


One seemingly innocuous mistake people may make when designing a kiosk for accessibility is automatically assuming that a touchscreen is the only way to interact with the kiosk. Even though touchscreens are often preferred by many users, they can be difficult or even impossible for people with certain disabilities to use. For example, individuals with low vision, motor disabilities, and certain communication impairments may not be able to use a touchscreen.

Therefore, it's important to provide alternate input methods, such as a keyboard and mouse, for people with disabilities. This will enable them to interact with the kiosk and access the same information and services available to people who don't have disabilities. For example, providing a keyboard or mouse option can enable people with motor disabilities to navigate the kiosk more easily. Similarly, a keyboard input may be helpful for people with speech disabilities, who may have difficulty using a touchscreen.

It's also important to keep in mind that input methods need to be optimized for accessibility. For example, a standard keyboard may not be suitable for people with motor disabilities, so a more specialized keyboard with larger keys and a more ergonomic design may be a better option. Similarly, for people who cannot use a standard mouse, a specialized mouse with more sensitive buttons and adjustable settings may be more accessible.

A further mistake people may make is not considering the complexity of kiosks. It's essential to ensure that the kiosk design is simple and easy-to-understand. This will make it easier for people with disabilities to understand how to interact with the kiosk. Simple designs can also reduce the risk of user frustration and errors, which can be especially detrimental for people with disabilities.

In conclusion, it's important to ensure that people with disabilities can access and use a kiosk. Designing kiosks with alternate input methods, such as a keyboard or mouse, and keeping the design simple are both essential to ensure people with disabilities can use the kiosk. Failing to consider these important factors can have serious consequences, preventing people with disabilities from accessing the same information and services as everyone else.